JOHN BARBER

Au & Ag

HEAP AND DUMP LEACHING PRACTICE

WITH

PANEL DISCUSSION

WATER CHEMISTRY OF HEAP LEACHING OPERATIONS

**Proceedings from the 1983 SME Fall Meeting
Salt Lake City, Utah, October 19-21, 1983**

EDITOR
J. Brent Hiskey

D1616598

SPONSORED BY

**SOLUTION MINING COMMITTEE
MINING AND EXPLORATION DIVISION
SOCIETY OF MINING ENGINEERS OF AIME**

Copyright © 1984 by the
American Institute of Mining, Metallurgical,
and Petroleum Engineers, Inc.

Printed in the United States of America
by Guinn Printing Co., Hoboken, New Jersey

All rights reserved. This book, or parts thereof, may not be
reproduced in any form without permission of the publisher.

Library of Congress Catalog Card Number 84-71234
ISBN 0-89520-425-8

PREFACE

This volume is the latest contribution by the Solution Mining Committee which focuses on topics germane to the broad field of solution mining. Past programs have been organized as topical minisymposia devoted to commodities of current interest and to advances in technology. These minisymposia have provided researchers and operators with valuable information, and have also served as a forum for cross-fertilization and technology exchange. The most recent programming effort in this series was the symposium on heap and dump leaching practice held at the 1983 SME Fall Meeting in Salt Lake City, Utah.

Heap and dump leaching was selected as the theme of this meeting because of Salt Lake City's proximity to the world's largest copper dump leaching operation, and its centrality to major gold and silver heap leaching operations in Nevada, New Mexico, and Montana. The intent of the program was to include all commodities and to cover the technology spectrum from fundamental to practical aspects of heap and dump leaching. However, the response to the call for papers and the numerous inquiries received indicated an overwhelming interest in the heap leaching of gold and silver. This was naturally justified because of the continued strength in precious metal activities and the overall attractiveness of heap leaching as a process alternative. Therefore, the final program reflected those interests. Thirteen of the fifteen papers presented at the meeting dealt with gold and silver leaching and recovery.

Under the leadership of Robert S. Shoemaker and Larry D. Hartzog, a panel discussion on water chemistry of heap leaching operations was organized for the 1983 SME Fall Meeting. John Dasher presented the keynote address for this session, and four panelists (Paul Chamberlin, Nerco Minerals; Jim Gourdie, Goldfield Mining Corp.; Roger Leonard, Cyprus Northumberland Mining Company; and Eric Daniels, Tenneco Minerals) discussed their respective operations and replied to questions from the panel moderators and the audience. Besides reviewing specific problems related to scaling, fouling, and water treatment measures at the various plants, the panel discussion provided valuable information about the different heap leaching operations and recovery circuits. The transcript of this session has been carefully edited for inclusion in this volume. In addition, two other papers on mercury removal from gold cyanide leach solution and experimental statistical optimization of zinc precipitation parameters have been incorporated into this book because they compliment the other papers and present valuable information in their own right. In addition, a brief introductory chapter is included to provide an overview of gold and silver leaching in the United States.

Judging from the session attendance, average 250, and the feed back after the conference, the heap and dump leaching symposium and water chemistry panel discussion were true programming successes.

J. Brent Hiskey   February 23, 1984
Chairman and Editor

CONTRIBUTING COMMITTEES

□□□□□□□□□

HEAP AND DUMP LEACHING SYMPOSIUM

SOLUTION MINING COMMITTEE

Daryl R. Tweeton, Chairman

Larry Sevenker, Programming

Paul Chamberlin, Program Planning

Jonathan S. Jackson, Publications

Peter G. Chamberlain, Member-at-Large

Clement K. Chase, Member-at-Large

J. Brent Hiskey, Past Chairman

□□□□□□□□□

WATER CHEMISTRY OF HEAP LEACHING OPERATIONS PANEL DISCUSSION

Robert S. Shoemaker, Chairman

Larry D. Hartzog, Chairman

□□□□□□□□□

The committees are most appreciative of the time and effort contributed by the authors in preparing their presentations and manuscripts. The committees would like to acknowledge Myrna R. Anderson, Fred C. Dunford and D. Scott Carruthers of Kennecott; James I. Christie of Bechtel; and Marianne Snedeker of the Society of Mining Engineers for their assistance in preparing this volume.

TABLE OF CONTENTS

TABLE OF CONTENTS (Continued)

Chapter 1

CURRENT STATUS OF U.S. GOLD AND SILVER HEAP LEACHING OPERATIONS

J.B. Hiskey
Process Technology
Kennecott Corporation
Salt Lake City, Utah 84147

ABSTRACT

Heap leaching has in recent years been established as an important processing alternative for gold and silver. Currently, heap leaching accounts for about 25% of primary mine produced gold and 10% of primary silver. This paper reviews gold and silver heap leaching practice and surveys major operations in the United States.

INTRODUCTION

Heap leaching has in the last decade established itself as an efficient method of treating oxidized gold and silver ores. This processing technique is an expedient way of extracting precious metals from small shallow deposits, but is especially appropriate for treating large low-grade "disseminated" deposits. In comparison to conventional milling, the combined capital and operating costs of heap leaching are normally lower, start-up times are faster, and leaching operations are environmentally safer. These advantages are sometimes offset by lower metal extractions with heap leaching.

The first application of cyanide heap leaching for gold and silver recovery may have been performed anonymously. However, the first commercial success was the heap leaching of mine cut-off material by the Carlin Gold Mining Company in northern Nevada. Early contributions to heap leaching technology by the U.S. Bureau of Mines provided impetus to the U.S. mining industry for developing the heap leaching process. (1-4) The continued high prices of gold and silver has sustained interest in the heap leaching method.

As a result of this interest, new developments and major advancements in heap leaching technology continue to come forth. In recent years numerous innovations have occurred in such areas as feed preparation (agglomeration), heap design and construction, solution distribution, and metal recovery.

The next paper (5) in the volume reports how some of these modifications have improved heap leaching performance and efficiency. A following paper (6) describes some pioneering efforts in heap leaching that have redefined the limits of low grade "ore." This large scale heap leaching operation is processing ore containing only 0.79 g/mt (0.023 oz/ton) gold.

In addition to leaching as-mined material, heap leaching has been demonstrated as a viable approach to processing agglomerated flotation tailings (7), and has been suggested for the treatment of coarse rejects from a SAG mill grinding circuit. (8)

DESCRIPTION OF OPERATIONS

According to Potter and Salisbury, (9) to be amenable to heap leaching a gold bearing rock should be competent, porous, relatively cyanicide free, and contain fine grained clean gold particles. The same considerations are important to the successful heap leaching of silver ores. Furthermore, clay content must be low enough to maintain adequate percolation of leach solutions and to keep mineral surfaces accessible to leach solutions. Kappes (10) has discussed the heap leaching of high clay gold ores in Costa Rica under conditions of excessive precipitation.

Since precious metal ore bodies vary significantly in geology, mineralogy, and metallurgy, it is difficult to generalize about flow sheet design. However, like other solution mining methods, heap leaching is more sensitive to site-specific factors such as topography and space, climatic conditions, availability of construction materials (i.e., clay for pad liners), environmental restrictions, and water. Heap leaching, because of its natural simplicity and flexibility is ideally suited to solve these design problems.

Leaching

There are basically two variations of the heap leaching methods which are used on a commercial scale. One involves leaching ore in the run-of-mine condition. Usually associated with this approach are relatively long leaching cycles. The other variation is based on the leaching of crushed ore and normally involves shorter leach cycles. High grade materials generally justify the added cost of crushing and are often expressly treated to maximize gold and silver recovery by providing good exposure of ore minerals to the leaching solution. Low grade ore is usually treated at run-of-mine sizes. An excellent example is the leaching operation of Zortman-Landusky Mining Company in the Little Rockies District of central Montana. (6)

Heap leaching operations that employ crushing typically leach ore crushed to -19.1 mm (3/4 in.) and possibly as fine as 6.35 mm (1/4 in.). The leach cycle for this kind of plant runs from a few weeks to several months. Most ores not containing an excessive amount of clay will be permeable to percolating solutions down to approximately 10 mm (0.39 in.). However, feeds below this size or containing a high proportion of clay can be treated by agglomerating techniques which stabilize fines. Besides maximizing percolation rates, agglomeration when performed with the lixiviant results in intimate contact between concentrated leaching solution and the ore. This usually produces faster leaching rates and higher recoveries of gold and silver.

The leach cycle of run-of-mine uncrushed ore is generally measured in terms of months or years. The size of the ore is that produced by blasting and/or ripping. It is reasonable that feed to this kind of heap may be -152 mm (6 in.), but may contain large boulders. Standard agglomeration techniques are not an effective means of stabilizing fines in coarse ores. Basic features of heap leaching operations treating run-of-mine and crushed ore are compared in Table 1.

TABLE 1
COMPARISON OF BASIC FEATURES
OF GOLD HEAP LEACHING

Feature	Run-of-Mine	Crushed
Particle Size	-150 mm	-20 mm to -10 mm
Grade	Low to Medium 1 to 1.7 g/mt	Medium 1.7 to 3.4 g/mt
Agglomeration	Not effective	If required
Leach Cycle	Months to years	Days to months
Gold Recovery	50-70%	60-90%

The ore is delivered to specially prepared impermeable drainage pads. The leach pad serves two important purposes: 1) to collect and eliminate loss of pregnant solution; and 2) to protect the environment. Several types of materials are commonly used to construct leach pads including both natural and man-made substances (i.e., synthetic membranes and fabrics). Single use pads are often constructed from clay or plastic liners, whereas multi-use pads are best made from asphalt or reinforced concrete. In all cases, pad construction must involve careful preparation of the sub-base and base. A network of perforated pipes is placed on the pad to collect pregnant leach solution. These pipes are covered with a protective layer of coarse gravel.

There are a number of techniques for placing ore on the leaching pad. Chamberlin (11) has discussed some of the methods of constructing heaps as they relate to maximizing permeability and leaching efficiency. The actual construction method often depends on the heap height to be used which in turn is sensitive to the length of the leach cycle and the available pad area.

Solution distribution is an important aspect of every heap leaching operation. Leach solution is applied to the surface of heaps by a variety of methods including spraying and sprinkling from plastic pipes, and flooding/ponding. The most popular systems use the impulse sprinkler (rainbird type) or the wobbler type sprinkler head. Solution application rate is a critical parameter. For typical heap leaching operations, the maximum effective application rate is 4 cm/hr (1 gal./sq ft/hr). (12) Higher application rates restrict the movement of oxygen through the rock pile, dilute the pregnant solution grade, and increase pumping costs. Solution application rates for heap leaching generally range between 0.8 and 1.2 cm/hr (0.2 and 0.3 gal./sq ft/hr).

A detailed analysis of the dissolution chemistry for gold and silver heap leaching must include information about the geological and mineralogical relationships of the ore. For simplicity, uniform oxidized ores derived geochemically from hydrothermal cells will be considered. Gold and silver occur mainly along fracture surfaces. Crushing exposes some of the gold and silver directly and allows ready access of the lixiviant. On these surfaces, dissolved values are recovered by simple surface flushing. Leach solution will penetrate particle fractures by capillary action; in this domain long-range diffusion must occur.

The active lixiviant for gold and silver leaching is an alkaline cyanide solution. As shown in the reaction below, oxygen (good aeration) is also required:

$$2Au + 4NaCN + \frac{1}{2} O_2 + H_2O \rightarrow 2Au(CN)_2^-$$
$$+ 2Na^+ + 2NaOH$$

A similar reaction can be written to describe the dissolution of native silver. Silver often exists as minerals other than native silver. The dissolution of argentite

(Ag_2S) and cerargyrite ($AgCl$) occurs according to the following reaction

$$Ag_2S + 4NaCN \rightarrow 2Ag(CN)_2^- + 2Na^+ + Na_2S$$

and

$$AgCl + 2NaCN \rightarrow Ag(CN)_2^- + Na^+ + NaCl$$

As shown, these minerals do not require oxidizing conditions for dissolution and are very amenable to direct cyanidation.

Gold and Silver Recovery

There are two primary commercial methods of recovering gold and silver from alkaline cyanide heap leach solutions-zinc dust (Merrill-Crowe) precipitation and adsorption by activated carbon. In addition to conventional recovery approaches (carbon-in-column and Merrill-Crowe) some emerging technologies (resin-in-column, direct electrowinning, and solvent extraction) (13) show promise.

The choice between carbon adsorption and zinc precipitation depends on several factors including:

- solution concentration
- solution volume
- solution clarity

As summarized by Potter, (14) very large volumes of low grade solutions, mainly containing gold, may be economically treated by carbon adsorption. Whereas, small flows of relatively rich solutions, or solutions containing large quantities of silver should be treated by zinc dust precipitation. The feed solutions to a carbon adsorption circuit do not have to be clarified. Solution clarification is vital for optimal efficiency of the zinc precipitation process.

Merrill-Crowe zinc dust precipitation is a very mature and well known technology. The process consists of solution clarification, deaeration, precious metal precipitation, and precipitate filtration. Cementation of gold onto a metallic zinc surface is represented by the following reaction:

$$2Au(CN)_2^- + Zn \rightarrow 2Au + Zn(CN)_4^{2-}$$

Zinc consumption is an important consideration in the operation of a Merrill-Crowe circuit. Based on the stoichiometry of the above reaction the theoretical zinc requirement is equivalent to 0.17 g Zn/g Au precipitated. In practice zinc consumption varies with the chemical character of the solution. For dilute heap leach solutions it may range between 10 and 30 g Zn/g Au. The excess is attributed to impurities and dissolved oxygen.

Zinc precipitation is the preferred process for silver ores because of the high silver concentrations and the poor silver-loading characteristics of carbon. Zinc precipitation is also ideal for small volumes of solution which can be treated by modular Merrill-Crowe units.

A continuous multi-stage carbon adsorption circuit is an efficient low cost method of recovering gold and silver from heap leach solutions. In a typical operation, pregnant solution is pumped countercurrently to activated carbon in a series of 5 or more columns. Proper carbon bed fluidization is achieved using an upward flow rate of 36 to 60 m/hr (15 to 25 gpm/ft^2) and carbon size from 16x30 mesh. At this size carbon adsorption kinetics do not limit the operation. Carbon is advanced through the circuit at a rate necessary to achieve loadings in the range of 3430 to 6860 g/mt (100 to 200 oz/ton). Excessive loading generally results in gold losses to the barren solution.

Loaded carbon is advanced from the first stage of the adsorption circuit to stripping. Stripping methods are summarized in Chapter 10 of this volume. (13) The popular stripping methods involve variations of

-   Hot, atmospheric NaOH, NaCN
-   Pressure NaOH, NaCN
-   Alcohol stripping

Dore' is usually recovered from the rich strip solution by electrowinning onto steel wool cathodes.

Carbon reactivation is commonly practiced in most recovery operations to remove surface contaminants and to restore the intrinsic chemical activity of the carbon. Regeneration involves a series of chemical and thermal treatments: acid washing to remove surface deposits like calcium carbonate, and calcining (750°C indirectly) to activate surface sites. The carbon is then screened to remove fines and returned to the adsorption circuit.

SURVEY OF OPERATIONS

Major Western U.S. gold/silver heap leaching operations have been surveyed. The locations of these operations are shown as solid symbols in Figure 1. In addition, this map indicates the locations of other plants described in this volume (Darwin, Mercur), but not specifically surveyed. Information and data for the various heap leaching operations was obtained by personal contacts and from the available literature. This information is summarized in Table 2.

Candelaria is definitely the largest producer of heap leach silver, producing some 81,000 kg (2.6 million oz) of silver annually. The Alligator Ridge and Zortman-Landusky mines are the largest heap leach producers of gold, each producing about 2,200 kg (70,000 oz) of gold annually. At Zortman-Landusky, silver is an important co-product, equalling about 3,900 kg (125,000 oz) per year.

From the data in Table 2 it is estimated that 10,640 kg (342,000 oz) of gold and 94,806 kg (3 million oz) of silver are currently produced by these operations. Based on these figures, heap leaching accounts for about 25% of the gold and 10% of the silver produced from domestic mines. By comparison, Chamberlain and Pojar (15) reported that 3,390 kg (109,000 oz) of gold and 4,074 kg (131,000 oz) of silver were recovered from heap leaching operations in 1979. At that time, these values corresponded to 10.6% of the gold and only 0.3% of the silver produced annually in the U.S. They projected that by the end of 1982, gold heap leach production would reach 7,775 kg (250,000 oz) per year and silver 124,400 kg (4 million oz) per year.

The growth in gold heap leach production has surpassed these estimates. On the other hand, silver heap leach production has grown substantially, but has not reached the predicted output. These growth trends will likely be maintained over the next few years with some heap leach projects already scheduled (Buckhorn and Relief Canyon in Nevada and Mesquite in California) and other likely candidates in the wings.

As our working experience with heap leaching becomes more developed, deciding whether to select heap leaching for a given deposit instead of conventional milling becomes easier. Nendick (16) provides some valuable rule-of-thumb guidelines for this evaluation. In one case, he uses a relationship between operating capacity and ore grade to demonstrate the relative domains of heap leaching vs conventional milling. Heap leaching is generally favored as expected by low grades and small tonnages.

It is instructive to examine this in terms of fundamental quantities that describe ore bodies (i.e., ore reserves and grade). These values have been plotted for six operating heap leach plants and six conventional mills in Figure 2. If linear regression is applied to all of the data, a boundary between heap leaching and conventional milling is clearly formed. The selection of the processing method seems to be related to the size and grade of the deposit; this was discussed in general terms earlier in this paper. Quantitatively, the data in Figure 2 show that for a 100 million mt ore body, the gold reserve must be at least 200,000 kg (6.4 million oz) to justify building a mill. On the other hand, a 10 million mt ore body must contain 38,000 kg (1.2 million oz) of gold to construct a milling circuit. The Golden Sunlight plant appears to be a borderline example. This deposit contains an estimated 46 million mt of 2.06 g/mt (0.06 oz/ton) gold and appears to be an ideal candidate for heap leaching. However, in the Golden Sunlight evaluation, heap leaching was rejected because of low gold extractions associated with the leaching of coarse ore particles.

Metallurgical and engineering factors are extremely important in determining the choice between conventional milling and heap leaching. It is hoped that the discussions and data presented in the following chapters will help provide valuable insight into the technical aspects of heap leaching.

Figure 1. Major Western U.S. Gold/Silver Heap Leaching Operations

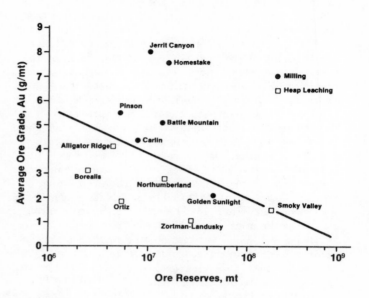

Figure 2. Grade Plotted as a Function of Ore Reserves for Selected Gold Ore Bodies

TABLE 2

HEAP LEACHING PLANT OPERATIONS

Mine	Mining Rate mtpy	Grade, g/mt		Pregnant Solution			Production, kg/year		Recovery Technique
		Au	Ag	Flow Rate liter/min.	Analysis, ppm Au	Ag	Au	Ag	
Alligator Ridge	680,000	4.11	N/A	3,785	1.0	--	2,177	--	CIC/EW
Bootstrap	200,000	1.51	N/A	950	1.0-3.7	--	187	--	CIC/EW
Borealis	500,000	3.09	17.0	1,500	1.0	--	933	--	MC
Candelaria	1,800,000	Minor	108	9,085	--	26	--	81,000	MC
Gold Acres	900,000	1.23	N/A	2,082	0.86	--	622	--	CIC/EW
Maggie Creek	450,000	1.0-2.1	N/A	1,136	0.68	--			CIC/EW
Northumberland	800,000	2.74	13.7	1,893	1.0	1.4	1,244	2,177	CIC/EW
Ortiz	680,000	1.82	Minor	3,217	1.0	--	1,089	--	CIC/EW
Pinson			***	See Chapter 5 for available information ***					
Smoky Valley	1,800,000	2.06	2.40	6,056	0.86	0.43	1,866	933	CIC/EW
Tombstone	450,000	0.50	34.3	680	0.3-0.45	10-17	158	4,631	MC
Tuscarora	90,000	0.69	60.0	870	0.30	10-15	31	2,177	MC
Windfall	200,000	0.96	Minor	567	0.70	--	156	--	CIC/EW
Zortman-Landusky	3,270,000	1.03	N/A	4,921	2.00	--	2,177	3,888	MC

REFERENCES

1. Heinen, H. J. and Porter, B., 1969, "Experimental Leaching of Gold from Mine Waste," Bureau of Mines RI 7250.

2. Potter, G. M., 1969, "Recovering Gold from Stripping Waste and Ore by Percolation Cyanide Leaching," Bureau of Mines TPR 20.

3. Heinen, H. J., Peterson, D. G., and Lindstrom, R. E., 1978, "Processing Gold Ores Using Heap Leach - Carbon Adsorption Methods," Bureau of Mines IC 8770.

4. Heinen, H. J., McClelland, G. E., and Lindstrom, R. E., 1979, "Enhancing Percolation Rates in Heap Leaching of Gold-Silver Ores," Bureau of Mines RI 8388.

5. DeMull, T. J. and Womack, R. A., "Heap Leaching Practice at Alligator Ridge," Chapter 2, this volume.

6. Roper, E. C., "Pegasus' Gold Ltd., Gold/Silver Operations at Zortman, Montana," Chapter 3, this volume.

7. Milligan, D. A. and Englehardt, P. R., "Agglomerated Heap Leaching Anaconda's Darwin Silver Recovery Project," Chapter 4, this volume.

8. Keuhey, K. Y. and Coughlin, W. E., "Getty Mining Company's Approach to Heap Leaching of the Mercur Mine," Chapter 6, this volume.

9. Potter, G. M. and Salisbury, H. P., 1974, "Innovations in Gold Metallurgy," Mining Congress Journal, July 1974.

10. Kappes, D. W., 1983, "Heap Leaching a High Clay Gold Ore in a Tropical Setting at Minera Maculona, Costa Rica," Paper presented at the Heap and Dump Leaching Symposium, SME Fall Meeting, Salt Lake City, Utah, October 1983.

11. Chamberlin, P. D., 1981, "Heap Leaching and Pilot Testing of Gold and Silver Ores, "Mining Congress Journal, April 1981.

12. Schlitt, W. J., "The Role of Solution Management in Heap and Dump Leaching," Chapter 8, this volume.

13. Mooiman, M. B., Miller, J. D., Hiskey, J. B., and Hendriksz, A. R., "Comparison of Process Alternatives for Gold Recovery from Cyanide Leach Solutions," Chapter 10, this volume.

14. Potter, G. M., 1981, "Design Factors for Heap Leaching Operations," Min. Eng., March 1981, p. 280.

15. Chamberlin, P. G. and Pojar, M. G., 1981, "The Status of Gold and Silver Leaching Operations in the United States," Gold and Silver - Leaching, Recovery and Economics, eds. W. J. Schlitt, W. C. Larson, and J. B. Hiskey, SME-AIME, New York, p. 1.

16. Nendick, R. M., "Engineering Design for the Recovery of Precious Metals from Heap Leach Solutions," Chapter 9, this volume.

Chapter 2

Heap Leaching Practice at Alligator Ridge

T.J. DeMull
R.A. Womack
Amselco Minerals, Inc.
Alligator Ridge Mine
P.O. Box 149
Ely, Nevada 89301

Abstract

More than 1.81 mt (2 million tons) of low grade ore have been heap leached at the Alligator Ridge mine. Since inception of leaching in 1980, several modifications have been made to ore agglomeration, heap construction, and leach operation practice. These modifications have improved the percolation rate of the ore and the rate of gold extraction from the ore. Changes made in each of these areas are described and the effects of the changes are discussed.

INTRODUCTION

The Alligator Ridge Mine is located 70 miles northwest of Ely in White Pine County, Nevada. Development of the mine began in the late 1970's as a joint venture between Amselco Minerals, Inc. and Occidental Minerals Corporation, with Amselco as the operating partner. Early in 1983 Nerco Minerals Company acquired Occidental's share of the property. The mine and ore processing facility have operated at capacity since 1981 producing 680,000 tonnes of ore and 1,900 kg of gold per year.

The gold ore deposits at Alligator Ridge consist of disseminated micron-size gold particles in a silicified siltstone matrix. The deposit comprises three separate but adjacent areas of mineralization that are designated as Vantage 1, Vantage 2, and Vantage 3 after the name of the basin in which the deposits lie.

The ore bodies are mined by open pit methods. Material is classified as ore, low grade, carbon ore, or waste using assays of blast hole drill cuttings. Carbon ore and low grade are stockpiled. Ore is direct hauled to the crushing plant. The average grade of ore mined to date has been 4 g Au per ton and has contained varying amounts of such deleterious constituents as clay, sulfide minerals, and carbon.

Gold is recovered from the ore by heap leaching. Ore is crushed to -19 mm in a three-stage crushing plant. Crushed ore is agglomerated with additions of water, cyanide, and lime in a rotating drum agglomerator. The agglomerated ore is hauled by truck and placed on the leach heaps. Dilute cyanide solution sprayed on top of the heaps percolates through and is collected by a drainage system beneath the heaps. Pregnant solution flows to a storage pond from which it is pumped to a series of five adsorption columns where gold is adsorbed on activated carbon. Gold is desorbed from loaded carbon in pressure vessels using a hot solution of concentrated cyanide and caustic soda. Rich liquor from desorption is processed for gold recovery by electrowinning on steel wool cathodes. Dore gold bars are produced from the cathodes in a refinery at the mine.

Ore processing commenced at Alligator Ridge in 1980. Since that time over two million tonnes of ore have been crushed and placed under leach. Efforts to improve gold recovery from the heaps have effected a number of operational changes in the areas of ore preparation, heap construction, and heap operation. Some of the changes made and the effects of the changes on solution percolation and gold extraction rate will be discussed.

HEAP LEACHING - BACKGROUND

Heap leaching has been defined as "the percolation leaching of piles of low grade ore that have been stacked or piled on specifically prepared water tight drainage pads for collection of preg-nant solution" (Heinen, H.J., Peterson, D.G. and Lindstrom, R.E., 1978). For the purposes of this paper, add to the above definition that leach solution is applied to the heap by spraying or sprinkling. Given a material of suitable porosity to allow diffusion of the lixiviant into and out of ore particles, successful heap leaching depends on obtaining maximum exposure of ore particles to solution flowing through the heap. Two criteria must be satisfied to assure maximum exposure of ore to lixiviant: (1) heaps must be uniformly permeable to solution flow and (2) solution must be uniformly distributed over the surface of the heap.

Permeability of an ore heap is affected by ore preparation techniques and heap construction methods. Low or non-uniform heap permeability may cause any of the following problems during leach-ing: Ponding of solution on top of the heap, chan-nelling of solution through the heap, or break-out of solution through the side of the heap. Most operations prepare ore for heap leaching by crush-ing. Crushing is controlled to produce a minimum of fines, since an overabundance of fines reduces the overall permeability of the heaped ore. If fines generation is unavoidable, agglomeration of the crushed ore improves permeability. Segregation of the ore by particle size during heap construc-tion produces heaps of non-uniform permeability. Agglomerating the ore prior to placement on the heaps reduces the chances of segregation. Compac-tion of the ore during heap construction reduces the overall permeability of the heap, so construc-tion methods should be devised to minimize compaction.

Maintaining uniform distribution of solution over the heaps is as important as providing uni-formly permeable heaps. Uneven distribution of solution is seen as either dry spots or solution ponds on the surface of the heap. Proper choice of sprinkler head design, sprinkler spacing, and oper-ating pressure assures good distribution.

Bench scale and pilot testing of samples from the Vantage ore bodies demonstrated the feasibility of extracting gold from the ores by heap leaching. Details of the pilot heap tests have been reported previously (Chamberlin, P. D., 1981). Many of the ore preparation, heap construction, and leach operation techniques that had been used success-fully in the bench or pilot leach tests were incor-porated in the design specifications and outline of operating procedures for full scale heap leaching at Alligator Ridge. Unpredictable, inconsistent, and frequently disappointing leaching performance combined with unforeseen problems caused by varying ore types have necessitated modifications in opera-ting practices for ore preparation, heap construc-tion, and leaching operation.

ORE PREPARATION

Figure 1 shows a summary of ore preparation details for all leach heaps completed prior to June 1983. The ore placed on the initial leach heaps, heaps A through E, was prepared in a temporary crushing facility. Ore processed in the temporary

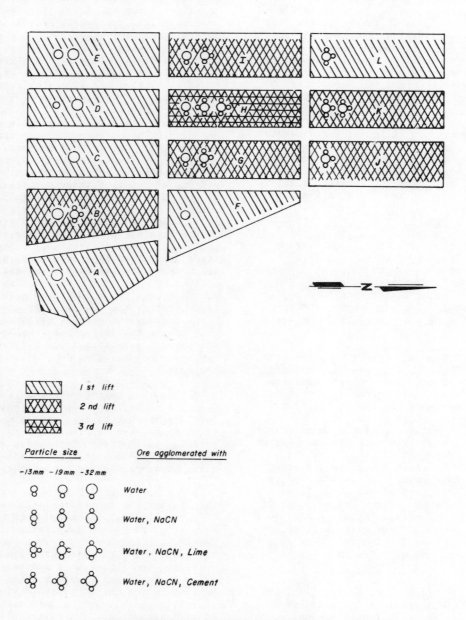

1 st lift

2 nd lift

3 rd lift

Particle size   Ore agglomerated with

−13mm −19mm −32mm

Water

Water, NaCN

Water, NaCN, Lime

Water, NaCN, Cement

Summary of ore preparation details for leach heaps
completed prior to June 1983

Figure 1.

crusher was crushed to either -32 mm or -13 mm and was not agglomerated. Ore placed on the remaining heaps has been prepared in the permanent crushing-agglomeration facility. Ore processed in the permanent crusher has been crushed to -19 mm and nearly all has been agglomerated. Additives used in agglomeration have included water, sodium cyanide, cement, and lime. These variations in crushing size and agglomeration practice have had varying impacts on leaching performance.

Crushing Size

As shown on Figure 1, ore processed at Alligator Ridge has been crushed to three different product sizes. To examine the effects of the three sizes on leaching performance, the results obtained on Heaps B, D, and F will be compared. Ore placed on Heap B was crushed to -32 mm, on Heap D to -13 mm, and on Heap F to -19 mm. Each of these heaps was constructed with non-agglomerated ore using the same construction techniques.

Both Heaps B and F performed well under leach. Neither exhibited extraordinary permeability problems. Both gold extraction rate and ultimate gold extraction from the heaps were satisfactory. During 1982, after leaching had been discontinued on both B and F, the leach residue on the heaps was sampled by drilling. Particle size analysis and assaying of the drill samples showed very little difference in the particle size distribution or gold content for the leach residues from the heaps. The residue from Heap B was expected to show a coarser particle distribution, but apparently the siltstone ore fragmentated during leaching. Crushing to the coarser size did not hamper leaching performance.

Much of the ore placed on Heap D was crushed to -13 mm. The extraction rate of gold from D was very slow because the finer-sized ore caused severe permeability problems. The heap never accepted solution well, even after it had been ripped between cycles of leaching with a 3 m ripper shank on a Caterpillar D-9L. While ripping on Heap D, lenses of fine particles were encountered that were large enough and dense enough to stall the dozer. These lenses probably originated during construction of the heap as the finer-sized, unagglomerated ore segregated into zones of coarse and fine particles. During leaching the lenses grew as fines migrated with the flowing leach solution and accumulated around the impermeable zones created by the segregated fines. The presence of the lenses caused channelling of solution through the heap, which reduced gold extraction rate from the ore. Ripping temporarily increased the gold extraction rate by establishing new flow paths through the impermeable zones. A satisfactory ultimate extraction was eventually obtained from Heap D after it had been ripped and releached four times.

Agglomeration

The ore placed on the initial heaps, Heaps A through F, was not agglomerated. The ore placed on all of the other heaps has been agglomerated. Water, sodium cyanide, cement, and lime have all

been used as additives in agglomeration. As agglomeration practice has changed, variations in leach performance of the heaps has been observed.

Unagglomerated Ore. Leaching performance of the heaps receiving unagglomerated ore varied from good to very disappointing. Heaps B, E, and F all exhibited adequate permeability, and gold extraction from each was satisfactory. In contrast, permeability problems were encountered during leaching of Heaps A, C, and D. Heap A showed the most severe problems. While leaching Heap A, solution ponds formed on top of the heap, ore sloughed from the sides of the heap, and solution channelled through the heap. The disappointing performance of Heap A was not caused solely by failure to agglomerate the ore. Heap construction methods and the high clay content of the ore also contributed to the poor permeability of the heap.

The inconsistent and unpredictable performance of the heaps receiving unagglomerated ore cannot be explained in terms of agglomeration practice only. While variations in ore particle size and heap construction contributed to the variable leach performance on Heaps A through F, the best explanation for the differences in performance were changes in the character of the ore.

Agglomeration with Water. The ore on the initial lifts of Heaps G and H was agglomerated with water. Leach performance of these heaps was very good; there were no permeability problems and gold extraction rate was satisfactory.

Experience has shown that the optimum water addition rate ranges from 20 to 40 kg per tonne, and the agglomerated ore typically contains 8% moisture. Water addition rate is manually controlled by the agglomerator operator based on visual indications in the crushing circuit. Too little water is seen as excessive dusting at conveyor transfer points while too much water causes rapid accumulation of sticky ore in conveyor transfer chutes.

Agglomeration with Cyanide. Results of comparative testwork performed during the metallurgical feasibility studies on the Vantage ores showed that agglomerating the ore with 250 g per tonne of sodium cyanide improved the initial extraction rate of gold during leaching. Performance of the heaps pretreated with cyanide at Alligator Ridge has generally confirmed the test results. Experimentation with the cyanide dosage rate has shown that 250 g per tonne of sodium cyanide was excessive. Good performance has been obtained on heaps pretreated with as little as 25 g per tonne and currently the addition rate to agglomeration is controlled at approximately 50 g per tonne.

Initially, agglomeration with cyanide was accomplished by adding leach solution, rather than water, to the agglomerator. The ore placed on Heap I and on the second lift of Heap H was agglomerated with leach solution, and the leach performance of both was superior to that of the heaps agglomerated with water only. The dosage rate of sodium cyanide to the ore when using leach solution was approximately 25 g per tonne.

On subsequent heaps the dosage rate was increased by injecting concentrated cyanide solution
into the leach solution feeding the agglomerator.
The ore placed on Heap K received 125 g per tonne
sodium cyanide and the ore on Heap J received 250 g
per tonne. Leach performance of K and J was no
better than that of H and I (caused in part by a
change in ore type), and overall cyanide consumption for K and J was much higher. Prior to
leaching, the ore on Heaps K and J consumed essentially all of the cyanide added in agglomeration,
and, during leaching, the ore consumed additional
cyanide from the leach solution. Based on that
experience, cyanide addition rate is currently
limited to 50 g per tonne. That dosage is adequate
to enhance gold extraction rate yet maintain
overall cyanide consumption at a reasonable level.

Agglomeration with Cement. The ore on the second
lift of Heap H was agglomerated with addition of
2.5 kg of cement per tonne. Initially, permeability of the heap was good, but later in the leaching
cycle permeability decreased. The reason for the
change in permeability has not been conclusively
determined. Near the end of the leach cycle, ponds
formed on the east side of the heap as solution
that could not permeate the ore flowed downgrade
and collected behind the perimeter berm. Even
though large ponds formed, the side of the heap did
not slough or wash out, perhaps because the cement
added in agglomeration stabilized the ore. Gold
extraction from the cement-agglomerated ore was
satisfactory.

Lime Agglomeration. Current practice at Alligator
Ridge includes substituting lime for cement in
agglomeration. Lime is not as persistent a binder
as cement, but does promote interparticle bonding
that improves ore permeability (McClelland, G. E.,
and Hill, S. D., 1981).

Lime has the additional advantage of providing
protective alkalinity for the leach solution. Some
of the ores processed at Alligator Ridge contain
acidic sulfide minerals that consume large quantities of caustic soda. Experience with those ores
has shown that caustic consumption rate can exceed
the capacity of the caustic make-up system. Currently the addition rate of lime in agglomeration
is manually adjusted between 1.5 kg per tonne and 5
kg per tonne depending on the requirements of the
ore. Since lime has been used in agglomeration, pH
control has improved and caustic make-up to the
leach solution has been practically eliminated.

The ore placed on the second lifts of Heaps, B,
G, I, J, and K has been agglomerated with lime and
sodium cyanide. These heaps have all exhibited
excellent permeability. None of the characteristic
indicators of poor permeability have been observed
on these second lifts, even though the solution
application rate is now twice the former rate.
Gold extraction rate has varied, since some of the
ore on the heaps has been mildly carbonaceous
and/or sulfide-bearing, but has generally been more
rapid than that observed for previous heaps.
Agglomeration of the ore with lime and cyanide has

contributed to these favorable results, but
improvements in heap construction methods (which
are discussed in the following section) have also
contributed to the favorable performance of the
heaps.

Summary of Agglomeration Practice. Some of the
heaps constructed with unagglomerated ore exhibited
poor permeability and slow gold extraction, while
others showed adequate permeability and satisfactory gold extraction. The heaps receiving ore
agglomerated with water performed well. Agglomeration of ore with cyanide increased the gold
extraction rate, but agglomeration of ore with high
dosages of cyanide resulted in inefficient utilization and excessive consumption of cyanide.
Cement agglomeration produced a mechanically stable
heap that performed well under leach. Agglomeration with lime has two advantages: Lime acts as a
binder in agglomeration and is a cheap source of
protective alkalinity that can be applied at
variable rates according to the specific needs of
the ore. Current practice at Alligator Ridge
includes agglomeration of ore with additions of 20
to 40 kg per tonne of water, 50 g per tonne of
sodium cyanide, and 1.5 to 5 kg per tonne of lime.
The quantities of water and lime are manually
adjusted within these ranges to meet the requirements of the ore. Agglomeration with this combination of additives has contributed to improvements
in heap permeability and gold extraction rate that
has made heap performance more consistent and more
predictable.

HEAP CONSTRUCTION

Figure 2 is a contour map of the leach pad area
showing the initial twelve leach heaps that were
constructed. The leach pad area, encompassing
approximately 0.3 sq km, was excavated adjacent to
the permanent crushing plant at a finished grade of
approximately 5% (sloping from north to south and
from west to east) to facilitate pregnant solution
drainage and collection. The pad liner comprised a
30 cm layer of compacted silt. The silt was
terraced to form the twelve separate leach pads
shown on the figure. Networks of slotted drainage
lines, covered with coarse gravel, were laid on top
of the silt for each pad. The drainage lines route
pregnant solution to the main collection pipes
installed along the east side of each pad. The
main collection pipes empty into Hypalon-lined
ditches running along the south end of each row of
pads.

The leach pads were installed as permanent,
single-use pads; i.e., after leaching was discontinued on a heap, the leach residue was to remain
in place on the pad while leaching commenced on
another heap. The space available for ore placement on the initial pad area shown on Figure 2 was
adequate for two years production, and preparation
of an estimated 1.0 sq km of additional leach pad
area was planned during the life of the mine.

Space limitations in the Vantage Basin coupled
with the high cost of pad preparation mandated
consideration of reusing the original pad area.

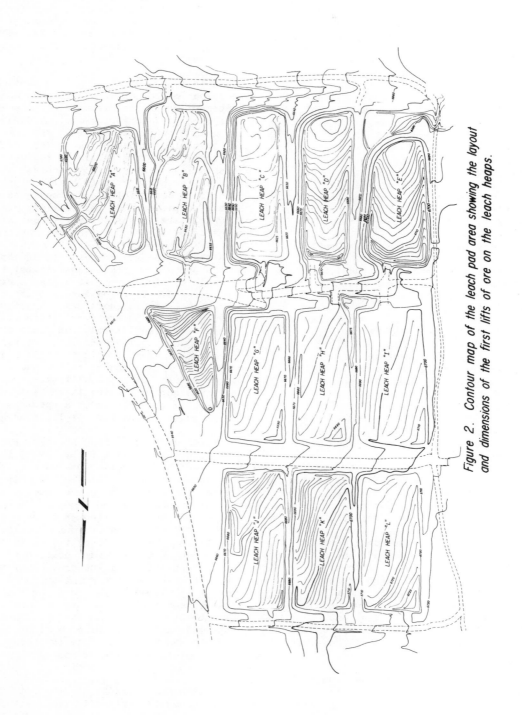

Figure 2. Contour map of the leach pad area showing the layout and dimensions of the first lifts of ore on the leach heaps.

Anticipating exhaustion of available pad space in late 1982, a consulting firm was commissioned in the spring of that year to study the feasibility of adding multiple lifts of ore to the existing leach heaps. The study examined the permeability and stability of the heaps and pad liner, and the probable effects the compaction pressure of additional lifts would have on the heap and liner material. It was concluded that placing ore on top of the existing heaps would decrease the permeability of both the heap material in place and the liner, but that the heap material showed adequate permeability and drainage characteristics to withstand the pressure of the additional lifts. Pursuant to the study, the decision was made to delay preparation of new leach pad area and extend the height of the existing heaps.

Most of the second lifts of ore have been constructed using a method different from that used for the first lifts. Performance of the first lifts was inconsistent and often disappointing. Performance of the second lifts has been consistently superior to that of the first lifts.

Construction and Performance of the First Ore Lifts

Figure 3 illustrates the techniques used to place ore on the first lifts of the heaps. On one end of each pad an external access ramp was built to the full height of the heap. Ore was placed on the pad by end dumping from trucks, advancing from the ramp across the entire width of the pad. During placement the ore was spread to desired grade with a dozer. When ore placement was completed, the top surface of the heap was thoroughly ripped and a berm was built around the perimeter of the top to prevent solution from running off and eroding the sides.

Although the majority of the first lifts were built to heights of approximately 4 m, some were built higher and some lower. No problems were experienced with the lower heaps, but ultimate extraction on Heap C, which was built to an average height of 6 m, was unsatisfactory. The heap exhibited poor permeability as a result of improper ore preparation and ore placement. Attempts to correct the permeability problems and improve gold extraction by ripping the heap were only partially successful. The heap was ripped on six occasions with a Caterpillar D-9L dozer fitted with a 3 m ripper shank. Auger drill sampling of the heap later showed that material reached by the ripper was thoroughly leached, while zones of ore grade material remained at depths greater than 3m. Ripping did improve the performance of Heap C, but it was not totally successful because the heap was built too high.

Most of the first lifts of ore did not accept solution at the design spray rate. Attempts at spraying the heaps at the design application rate of 0.003 l per sec per sq m resulted in excessive ponding of leach solution on the tops of the heaps. To prevent ponding it was necessary to reduce the application rate to approximately half the design rate. A persistent problem, even at reduced application rates, was formation of solution ponds near the edges of the heaps where sloughing or wash-out of the sides could occur. Study of Figure 2 shows the variety of slopes and configurations built into the tops of the heaps while attempting to prevent ponding near the edges. The most effective configuration was that used on Heap L, where the slope was 2% north to south and west to east, and a series of berms was built inside the perimeter berm. No large solution ponds formed on the top of L, and the sides of the heap were never threatened.

Another persistent problem with the first lifts was break out of solution from the sides of the heaps on, or in the vicinity of, the access ramps. Equipment traffic during ore placement caused heavy compaction of the material on the ramps and of the ore just off the end of the ramps. The effects of the compaction were partially relieved by ripping, which allowed solution to percolate through the heap to the depth reached by the ripper shank. Below that depth solution encountered a zone of highly compacted, low permeability ore, so it flowed laterally until it broke out either through the side of the heap or through the ramp.

Although the adverse effects of compaction were most apparent near the access ramps, the effects were not confined to those areas. Degradation and compaction of ore by equipment traffic decreased permeability and hindered gold extraction to varying degrees on the first lifts of all the heaps. Formation of solution ponds on the tops of the heaps during leaching, even at reduced solution application rates, provided tangible evidence that compaction by equipment traffic had reduced overall heap permeability. In addition, performance of the heaps was unpredictable; the effects of compaction on leaching performance of a specific heap could not be assessed until after leaching had begun.

Heap K was built using a method prescribed elsewhere (Chamberlin, P. D., 1981) in an attempt to reduce the compaction pressure on the ore during placement. Briefly, this method comprised building a central access road on the heap, dumping ore at the end of the road, and moving ore to the perimeter of the pad with a dozer. The ground pressure of a loaded haul truck is much greater than that of a dozer, so limiting truck travel to a narrow strip in the center of the heap should have reduced overall compaction of the ore. When the heap was completed, the central road was cut down and thoroughly ripped. Despite being built in this manner, Heap K showed no marked improvement in permeability compared to the other heaps. It is suspected that the combined action of ground pressure and vibration from the dozer caused as much compaction of the ore as truck traffic would have.

While some of the first ore lifts on the leach heaps performed very well, taken as a group the performance of the heaps was not satisfactory. The most disconcerting aspect of performance had been the inconsistencies from heap to heap. Agglomeration of ore had improved heap permeabilities, but improvements in heap construction methods that reduced compaction of the ore during placement were

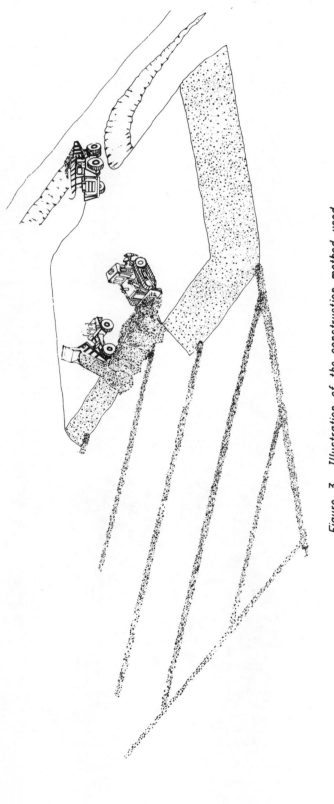

Figure 3. Illustration of the construction method used to place ore on the first lifts of the leach heaps.

Figure 4. Illustration of the construction method as modified for placing ore on the second lifts of the leach heaps.

also needed to further enhance leach performance.

Construction and Performance of the Second Ore Lifts

The decision to proceed with multiple lifting of ore on the heaps provided an opportunity to modify construction methods to reduce compaction. The modified methods are illustrated in Figure 4. An access ramp is constructed to the height of the existing heap, and the top of the heap is levelled and thoroughly ripped. Ore is end dumped in rows across the width of the heap, and the rows of ore are pushed together with a dozer to form the new lift. Before each row of ore is added to the new lift, the existing heap material beneath that row is ripped to relieve any compaction caused by equipment traffic. The final height of the new lift averages 2 m and the top surface consists of irregularly spaced ridges and furrows. Unlike the former construction method, fresh ore placed by the new method is not subjected to compaction by equipment traffic.

Second lifts of ore had been added to five heaps at the time of this writing. Leach performance of these lifts has been excellent. All have accepted solution at the design application rate and no ponding of solution has been observed. Gold extraction has been rapid; complete extraction has been obtained in 30 to 40 days, compared to 60 to 90 days, or longer, for heaps constructed by the former method. The ore placed on the second lifts has been agglomerated with lime and cyanide. The benefits of agglomeration and the improved construction method have combined to produce consistently superior leaching performance.

LEACH OPERATIONS

For the first two years of leach operations at Alligator Ridge, irrigation-type impulse sprinkler heads were used for spraying the heaps. Changing from impulse sprinklers to Senninger wobbler sprinklers has improved solution distribution and reduced the amount of leaching downtime needed for sprinkler maintenance. Permeability problems, and resulting low gold extractions, experienced on some of the early heaps caused a change in leaching practice. Alternate cycles of leaching, draining, ripping, and releaching of the heaps partially relieved inherently poor permeability and increased the ultimate gold extraction from the problem heaps.

Sprinkler Heads

The impulse sprinkler heads originally used at Alligator Ridge provided uniform distribution of solution on the heaps as long as the rotating motion of the sprinklers was not stalled. Stalling of rotation was a constant problem since it could occur for any of the following reasons: Inadequate operating pressure, plugging of the sprinkler orifice with scale or debris, wear on the moving parts of the head, or formation of ice on the head during subfreezing weather. Stalled impulse sprinklers caused dry spots on the heaps, and, if

the sprinkler orifices were not plugged, caused formation of solution ponds. Downtime for unplugging and freeing sprinklers adversely impacted gold production.

Late in the 1982 leaching season the impulse sprinklers were replaced by Senninger wobblers that were fitted with individual pressure regulators. Figure 5 is a photograph of the combination sprinkler-pressure regulator. Stalled sprinklers are less common now, and are easier to restart when stalled. Also, a stalled wobbler emits a spray of solution rather than a single stream, reducing the chances of pond formation. Since the wobblers have only one moving part, they are less susceptible to wear. The Senningers are also less sensitive to subfreezing temperatures; leaching continued without interruption into mid-December 1982 in spite of temperatures as low as -15°C in late November. Since installation of the wobblers, leaching downtime for sprinkler maintenance has been practically eliminated. Even though scaling of sprinkler heads has never been a serious problem at Alligator Ridge, an anti-scaling reagent is now added to the leach solution and has also contributed to the reduction in leaching downtime.

Figure 5. Photograph of Senninger wobbler sprinkler head and pressure regulator.

Addition of the pressure regulators to the system has simplified leach operation and improved solution distribution to the heaps. Formerly, solution distribution on the heaps was regulated by manually adjusting both system pressure at the pump and line pressure to the individual heaps. Adjusting the pressures to obtain uniform distribution was difficult and tedious because all the sprinklers were not at the same elevation (refer to Figure 2). As a result, regulating solution distribution on the heaps was a compromise between under-spraying some areas and over-spraying others. Since the installation of the pressure regulators on each sprinkler head, precise and tedious pressure adjustments are no longer required. Currently, it is necessary to adjust only the system pressure at the pump to provide adequate operating pressure for the highest elevation sprinklers. The regulators equalize pressure and flow at all sprinklers in the system, thus assuring uniform solution distribution over the entire area under spray.

Ripping the Heaps Between Leach Cycles

Observations concerning the beneficial effects of ripping heaps between leach cycles have been presented in previous sections of this paper. Ripping a heap between cycles of solution application breaks up existing solution flow paths and establishes new ones, thus exposing fresh ore to lixiviant. All of the heaps that have been ripped and releached have shown improved performance. For heaps that exhibited poor permeability, ripping was essential to attaining satisfactory gold extraction. Ripping has improved the performance even on those heaps that exhibited no permeability problems and yielded satisfactory gold extractions.

Ripping practice at Alligator Ridge has been as follows: (1) a heap is leached until the grade of solution returning from the heap falls below a specified economic cutoff level, (2) solution application is then halted and the heap allowed to drain, and (3) when dry enough for the dozer to work on top, the heap is thoroughly ripped lengthwise, laterally, and diagonally. A disadvantage of this procedure is that it can be very time consuming; experience has shown that it takes 30 days, or longer, to drain a heap. Heaps have been ripped with both a Caterpillar D-8 dozer fitted with a 1 m ripper shank and a Caterpillar D-9L fitted with a 3 m ripper shank. The most effective by far has been the larger dozer and longer shank.

Thus far, none of the second lifts of ore on the heaps has been ripped and releached. Since all of the second lifts have performed very well, practice has changed to ripping heaps before addition of another lift of ore. Since the second lifts of ore have averaged approximately 2 m in height, the 3 m ripper on the D-9L will effectively rip through the entire lift. Ripping is now an element of heap construction rather than heap operation.

SUMMARY

Heap leaching performance at Alligator Ridge has improved over the past three years from unpredictable, inconsistent, and frequently disappointing to predictable, consistent, and gratifying. During the first two years of operation, the most predictable and consistent aspects of heap performance were the recurring problems of poor permeability and slow gold extraction. Modifications in ore preparation, heap construction, and leaching operations practice have combined to eliminate many of the problems and improve gold extraction.

Almost all of the original heaps exhibited some degree of permeability problems. Reactionary measures such as experimenting with different slopes and configurations of the tops of the heaps and ripping the heaps between cycles of solution application were partially effective in overcoming the problems caused by poor permeability. These measures improved heap performance enough to allow production forecasts to be met, but were not wholly satisfying, since they treated the symptoms rather than the causes of poor permeability.

One cause of permeability problems was the segregation of ore particles by size during placement on the heaps. Agglomeration of crushed ore has helped to reduce segregation in the heaps at Alligator Ridge. Water, cyanide, cement, and lime have all been used as additives to agglomeration. The best leaching performance has been obtained using a combination of water, cyanide, and lime. Cyanide added during agglomeration increases the extraction rate of gold and lime acts both as a binder for fine particles and a source of protective alkalinity for the leach solution. Adjusting the water and lime addition rates to match the requirements of the ore has produced consistently good performance from a variety of ore types.

Another cause of permeability problems was compaction of the ore during heap construction. Trucks and dozers working on top of a heap compacted the ore and reduced permeability. The decision to add multiple lifts of ore on top of existing heaps provided an opportunity to modify the ore placement methods to reduce compaction during heap construction. Most of the second ore lifts have been built using the modified method. Characteristic indicators of poor permeability, such as ponding, and side slope break-out of solution, commonly seen on the first lifts, have not been observed on the second lifts, even though the solution application rate has been doubled. Elimination of permeability problems through the combined beneficial effects of current agglomeration and heap construction practice has produced more rapid and more predictable gold extraction.

Uniform solution application must also be maintained to assure successful heap leaching. The Rainbird impulse sprinklers orginally used at Alligator Ridge provided adequate solution distribution, but were susceptible to stalling of the rotating motion of the head. Stalled sprinklers adversely affected solution distribution and caused excessive downtime for maintenance. Changing to Senninger wobblers fitted with pressure regulators has improved solution distribution and reduced downtime.

ACKNOWLEDGEMENT

The authors wish to thank those people at the
Alligator Ridge Mine, Amselco Minerals, Inc. in
Denver, and BP Minerals International Ltd. in
London who helped in preparing and reviewing this
paper. A special acknowledgement is given to John
K. Grant at Alligator Ridge for preparation of the
drawings and assisting in composing the final copy
of the paper.

BIBLIOGRAPHY

Chamberlin, P. D., 1981, "Heap Leaching and Pilot
    Testing of Gold and Silver Ores", Mining
    Congress Journal, April, pp. 47-51.

Heinen, H. J., Peterson, D. G., and Lindstrom, R.
    E., 1978, "Processing Gold Ores Using Heap
    Leach-Carbon Adsorption Methods", IC 8770, U.
    S. Bureau of Mines, 21 pp.

Heinen, H. J., McClelland, G. E., and Lindstrom, R.
    E., 1979, "Enhancing Percolation Rates in Heap
    Leaching of Gold-Silver Ores", RI 8388, U. S.
    Bureau of Mines, 20 pp.

McClelland, G. E. and Hill, S. D., 1981, "Silver
    and Gold Recovery from Low-Grade Resources",
    Mining Congress Journal, May, pp. 17-23, 41.

Chapter 3

Pegasus' Gold Ltd., Gold/Silver Operations at Zortman, Montana

Edward C. Roper
Zortman-Landusky Mining Company
P.O. Box 313
Zortman, Montana 59546

Abstract

Pegasus' Gold Ltd. operates two gold/silver heap leaching operations in the Little Rockies area of Montana. The Little Rockies has produced gold from underground operations on an intermittent basis from the 1880's to the early 1950's and from the open-pits on a continuous basis since 1979. Run-of-the-mine ore is drilled, blasted, sorted, loaded and hauled. The waste is dumped and compacted into 30 meter (100 foot) fills to be used for future leach pads. The leach pads have a central drain system and the impermeable membrane is constructed of bentonite and 30 mil PVC. The plants which have been expanded to 4900 lpm (1300 gpm) capacity use the Merrill-Crowe process for gold and silver recovery. 4600 liters (1200 gpm) of the 9500 lpm (2500 gpm) spray capacity is recycled through the old leach pads for upgrading before being processed. The gold/silver precipitate is smelted and the resultant dore' is shipped to a buyer/refiner. 1983 projected production is 2,177 kg (70,000 ozs) of gold at a cost of less than $10/gm.

INTRODUCTION

Landusky Mining, Inc. and Zortman Mining, Inc. are two registered Montana Corporations wholly owned by Pegasus Gold, Ltd. of Vancouver, B.C. The Zortman and Landusky Mines are located in the Little Rockies District of central Montana.

The Zortman-Landusky mines produced 2,100 kg gold in 1982. A total of 3,300,000 mt of ore per year are mined during the period March 1 to September 15, at an average grade of 1.03 gm/mt (0.03 oz/t) gold and 13.2 gm/mt (0.385 oz/t) silver at a cutoff grade of 0.34 gm Au/mt of ore (0.01 oz of Au/t). The stripping ratio during 1983 is anticipated to be 0.75:1 waste to ore. Combined average plant capacity of the two Merrill-Crowe plants is 9,840 lpm (2,600 gpm). The combined heap spray capacity of the two plants approaches 18,900 lpm (5,000 gpm). The mine employs approximately 200 people, about half of these work for the mining companies and the other half for the mining contractor, N. A. Degerstrom of Spokane, Washington. Net profit in 1982 for Zortman and Landusky Mining, Inc. approximated $4,900,000 at an average gold price of $11.40/gm.

PHYSIOGRAPHY

The Little Rockies rise abruptly to about 914 m (3,000 ft) above the surrounding plains to 1,829 m (6,000 ft) above sea level. The topography is rugged, characterized by narrow canyons, peaks, cliffs, and steep walled valleys. The climate is semi-arid with moderate summers and severe winters. Freezing temperatures commonly extend from early November through April. As a result, leaching operations are limited to approximately 200 days each year.

GEOLOGY & MINERALOGY

The geology of the Little Rocky Mountains is relatively simple. Steeply dipping sedimentary ridges form an elliptical dome surrounding a core of mountains of an intruding syenite.

The syenites are extensively fractured and mineralization occurs at the intersection of strong shears. Movement has occurred along these shears before, during and after mineralization. Economic mineralization occurs in either higher grade veins or lower grade fracture stockworks. The mineralization is divided into four categories based on the type and degree of oxidation: 1) strongly oxidized; 2) weakly oxidized; 3) mixed oxide-sulfide; and 4) sulfide. Gold and silver are the only economic minerals.

The silver/gold ratios vary considerably between pits. The ratios in any one deposit have not shown any significant change with depth in the oxidized zones.

Mineralization appears most directly related to the mechanical behavior of the host rock. The more shattered and open fractures are the major host for gold-silver mineralization. Our current geological reserves are 28,636,000 mt (31,500,000 t) at 0.79 gm/mt (0.023 oz/t) gold. A more detailed discussion of the geology is given in the paper entitled Syenite Hosted Gold Deposits of the Little Rockies by L. M. Rogers and M. S. Enders.

HISTORY

Gold was first discovered in the Little Rocky Mountains in 1864 as placer deposits. Early hardrock mining did not begin until the 1880's and began with open stoping but rapidly changed to low cost, glory hole caving.

The extremely fine-grained gold caused recovery problems for both placer miners and early lode miners. Intensive development in the district did not begin until 1903 when the cyanide process was first introduced. Cyanide mills were constructed in Zortman in 1903 and Landusky in 1907, beginning a period of continuous operation in the district which lasted until low prices forced the mines to shut down in 1923.

An increase in the price of gold to $35/oz in 1934 spurred a small mining boom which lasted until 1942, when the War Production Board Order L-208 ended most gold mining. Sporadic efforts were made to reopen the mines after the war; but all serious mining had ceased by 1951. In 1979, mining once again began in the Little Rockies with the startup of the current open-pit heap leaching operation.

Total production from the Little Rocky Mountains is estimated at approximately 13,300 kg (428,000 oz) of gold through the end of 1951. Unfortunately, no figures are available for past silver production. The bulk of the production occurred between 1893 to 1942.

Mining in the past was restricted to the veins and higher grade stockwork. Mining grades during this period probably averaged about 2.7 gm/mt (0.08 oz/t) gold with the veins probably containing about 3.4-5.1 gm/mt gold (0.10-0.15 oz/t gold).

TODAY'S OPERATION

Mining

Commencing in 1979, the method of mining in the Little Rockies changed to open pit. Initial production was limited to 696,000 mt (766,000 t) of ore because of a lack of cash which resulted from a lack of confidence of the investing public in such a low grade deposit. Once it was shown that the mining and leaching could be done profitably, and cash reserves increased, the mining rate expanded each year, until 1982, when it reached its current annual rate of 3,309,000 mt (3,640,000 t) of ore per year.

Initial pit designing starts with exploration holes spaced at a maximum 30 m (100 ft) intervals, 6 m (20 ft) benches, and a cutoff grade of 0.34 gm/mt (0.010 oz/t) gold. Because of the low silver recoveries in the heaps, silver is currently not used in determining economic pits. Pits vary in size from 273,000-2,455,000 mt (300,000-2,700,000 t) ore with further push backs in the walls. Pit design is complicated because of the necessity of allowing for sufficient waste to construct next year's leach pad fills.

Once clearing of the pit has been done, drilling commences on a 4 m x 4 m (14 ft x 14 ft) blast pattern. Each hole is 8 m (25 ft) deep with 1.5 m (5 ft) of subgrade. All drill holes are surveyed for location in the pit. All drill cuttings are sampled for gold, silver, geology and leachability. After the holes have been blasted using high density slurry/ANFO mixture at a powder factor of 0.30 kg/mt (0.60 lb/t) of rock, ore/waste control ribbons are put in the field. Ore/waste boundaries are adjusted by the geology department for sulfides and degree of oxidation. Because of the fast pace of mining, ore/waste assays must be available to be placed in the field within 24 hours, and most times less, of the hole being drilled.

Waste is hauled to the next year's leach pad fills. All fill is placed in 1.5 m (5 ft) lifts, compacted by the mining equipment and designed at an overall slope of 2:1. Ore is hauled to the leach pad, dumped in 6-9 m (20-30 ft) lifts to a maximum of 30 m (100 ft). Each lift is cross-ripped to a depth of 1.5 m (5 ft) before leaching to reduce the affect of compaction on the ore.

Each leach pad is designed to hold up to 37.8 million liters (10 million gallons) of solution using the construction of a dike on the downstream side. All leach pads are designed with internal surface drains feeding a pipe through the dike. The impermeable layer of the pad is constructed of a fine rock base topped with 0.3 m (12 in.) of compacted bentonitic shale which is then covered with a 30 mil PVC blanket which is protected by 0.5 m (18 in.) of tailings. The 30 mil PVC is used because our investigations of the original pads showed that the carbon in the bentonitic shale absorbed gold and assayed 5.1 gm/mt (0.15 oz/t) gold. The tailings on top of the plastic is used to protect the plastic from run of the mine ore and is derived from the tailings of the old cyanide mills. These tailings assay around 0.64 gm/mt (0.018 oz/t) gold with sufficient recovery to pay for the hauling and placement on top of the plastic. Current leach pad construction costs are $0.75/mt of ore, with cost of waste overhaul beyond 610 m (2,000 ft) included in this cost.

Zortman-Landusky Mining, Inc.'s current mining, leach pad, ponds and plants, occupy a total of 1,295,000 m² (320 acres).

Generally, ponds are designed to hold 15,140,000 to 22,710,000 liters (4-6 million gallons). The pond is constructed of a fine rock base covered with 0.3 m (12 in.) of compacted bentonitic shale protected by 36 mil, 1000 denier, 10 x 10 reinforced hypalon. Side slopes of the ponds are 2-1/2:1.

All clearing of the pits, mining, construction of the pads, fills and ponds, and ripping of the ore on the leach piles is done by contract. The mining contractor, N. A. Degerstrom, Inc. of Spokane, employs: 1 - 992 front end loader; 2 - 245 hydraulic shovels; 1 - 988 B.F.E.L.; 1 - D-10 Cat; 5 - D-9 Cat; 3 - graders; 18 - 773 50-ton trucks; 5 - Ingersoll Rand 6-inch drills; and, 100 employees.

Plants

The two Merrill-Crowe plants have an average combined capacity of 9,800 lpm (2,600 gpm) and a combined sprinkler capacity approaching 19,000 lpm (5,000 gpm). Plant solution chemistry varies between Zortman and Landusky and what is good for one plant is not necessarily good for the other. Starting the circuit at the barren pond, a spray water pH of 11.0, and free cyanide level of 1.05 gpl (2.1 lb/t) of water is required for Zortman and a pH of 11.0 and free cyanide level of 0.80 gpl (1.6 lb/t) of water is required for Landusky. Each side has between 600 and 800 sprinklers operating at any one time, the number depending on the total number of Senninger impulse and wobbler sprinklers in use at the time.

During the winter of 1982-1983 we were able to extend the leaching season with the installation of buried PVC sewer pipe for our cyanide solution distribution system. This was a gravity fed system. We plan to use 4 cm (1-1/2 in.) pressure pipe during the 1983-84 season again to extend the leaching season but under pressure to improve on the distribution of the solution. Each side has a minimum of 7,315 m (24,000 ft) of 5 cm (2 in.) Yelomine distribution lines on top of the heaps. Because of previous problems with failures in the larger diameter Yelomine coupling, all uncontained cyanide water distribution lines are steel.

All heaps are designed with 30.5 cm (12 in.) interval drains which collect the leachate and feed the pregnant pond either by gravity or pump. Of the 18,925 liters (5,000 gal.) sprayed onto the heaps, approximately 5-10% is lost in evaporation, 9,800 lpm (2,600 gpm) of the highest grade solution is delivered to the pregnant pond, and the remaining lower grade solution is piped to the barren pond for recirculating and upgrading.

The pH, CN levels and Na/Ca ratio of the pregnant ponds vary between each side with Landusky being much more flexible. Optimum conditions at Landusky are a pH of 10.5, CN level of 0.37 gpl (0.74 lb/t) of water, and Na/Ca ratio of 41:1 with an Na content of 950 ppm. The Na/Ca ratio has been as high as 86:1. The Zortman levels must be much more exact with a pH of 10.2, CN level of 0.26 gpl (0.53 lb/t) of water and an Na/Ca ratio of less than 8:1 with an Na content of 800 ppm. We have adjusted the Na/Ca ratio with $CaNO_3$ and, to date, have found this a satisfactory method of adjusting the Na/Ca ratio. We, at present, do not know why the Na/Ca ratio is so critical at Zortman but we are currently testing to determine if this ratio is directly proportional to the amount of Ca available for flocculating of the fine particles in the pregnant pond. Our cyanide consumption in the heaps appears to be 0.35 kg NaCN/mt (0.70 lb/t) of fresh ore put on the heap. How this consumption will vary with the increased percentage of old ore being treated this year, we have not yet determined.

Solution from the pregnant pond is pumped into the plant and through two 150 m^2 (1,600 ft^2) sparkler filters. The resultant clarified solution is sampled for clarity using a Hach Turbidity Meter Model 15625 which measures down to a 1/10 of a ppm of clarity. The clarified solution must be "gin clear" in order to have a successful Merrill-Crowe process. The solution then goes into a 13 m^3 (462 ft^3) deaeration tower filled with helixes. Into the resultant deaerated solution at Zortman is fed: 9.2 grams of zinc/gram of dore' and 7.5 ml of $PbNO_3$/min.; and at Landusky: 6.9 grams of zinc/gram of dore' and 7.5 ml $PbNO_3$/min. This year we cut our zinc consumption by 1/2 to 1/3 by increasing our vacuum capacity from 142 cm^3/sec vacuum capacity/liter of treated water to 217 cm^3/sec vacuum capacity/liter of treated water. We have found that changing our zinc feeder to one which consistently gives an exact amount of zinc feed, improved our recovery 3%-5%. We currently use an Acrison zinc feeder.

A United Pump Model F-6x17VP with its impeller casing completely enclosed in a water bath feeds five 0.9 m x 0.9 m (34 in. x 34 in.) plate and frame zinc precipitate filters. Each plate and frame zinc filter has 72 plates and frames.

Each plant has an Instrument Laboratory Atomic Absorption machine which is used for hourly plant silver recovery testing. Silver recoveries are measured because there is less likelihood of interference in the measurements in the "rough" environment of the plant than there is with gold. If we maintain +98% silver recovery, then our gold recoveries will be +90%. These AA machines have helped to develop better plant operators and increased our gold recoveries. During 1982, pre-cipitate grades averaged 7%. With the increased vacuum capacity, the ability to control the Na/Ca ratio and improved zinc feed, the precipitate grade so far this year has averaged above 20% and have reached as high as 45% dore'. Each plant is able to obtain on a regular basis a gold recovery of around 90% with a plant feed as low as 0.21 grams of gold/t of water.

Once the solution has gone through the plant, it is sampled and discharged into the barren pond. Lime and/or caustic is added to the barren pond for pH control and NaCN briquettes for CN makeup.

Currently, we use the Gould Model XLT 3196 10 cm x 8 cm x 33 cm pumps for the spray, plant feed and leach pad discharge pumps. At any one time, Zortman will have 11 operating pumps plus 6 on line for immediate service if a pump was to fail. At Landusky the number is 9 operating and 5 spare. With the volumes of water handled, we cannot afford down time to replace a pump.

The total capital costs of our plants were approximately 2.5 million to construct and equip. Except for the building, all design, construction and equipping was done by Zortman-Landusky personnel.

We estimate total gold recovery in the ore heaps to approach 70% after three years. For silver, the recovery is estimated to be 30%.

Most of the plant recoveries and test work is analyzed using linear statistical mathematical modeling (see Chapter 11).

Refinery

Last year, our refinery was undersized because of the low precipitate grade. However, now that the precipitate grade has been increased (less zinc) it is anticipated that two propane-fired 57 kg (125 lb) charge Wabi's will be sufficient for 1983. The refinery will operate 8-10 hours per day, five days per week.

At the end of 1982, the refinery was producing a dore' assaying 32.5% gold, 62.5% silver and 5% slag. The slag assayed 309 gm/mt (9 oz/t) gold plus 813 gm/mt (23.7 oz/t) silver. We crush, screen and put through a "gold-hound" all bar slag. This slag is combined with the other slag produced during the day and shipped to the Asarco East Helena smelter in truck load lots. In 1982, we shipped 177 tons of slag.

Laboratory

Our laboratory is designed to handle 800 samples or 1,600 determinations per day. We do both AA and fire assaying. All production blast hole results must be assayed within 24 hours of being drilled. Each thirty sample load put through for assaying contains one duplicate, one sample to be run AA, or fire for check, and a low, average and high grade standard sample. In addition to our production blast hole assaying, we do all our own exploration, plant solution and most of our own test work analysis.

Our lab contains two drying ovens, two ring rollers, two fire furnaces, one cupelling furnace, two Model 4000 and one Model 303 Perkin Elmer AA machines. All assays are reviewed by the shift assayer, laboratory supervisor and the department requiring the assays in order to ensure assay accuracy. At a 0.34 gm/mt gold (0.01 oz/t gold) cutoff grade, we cannot afford errors.

In addition, we check each lot of the distilled water, MIBK, litharge, etc., before using. We have, for instance, received bad lots of MIBK which has affected our AA assay results.

Composite ore samples from the production drill cuttings are taken from each pit production bench and bottle rolled to determine gold and silver recoveries. The same is done for all ore intersections in our exploration holes. In addition to recoveries, each bottle roll sample is assayed for iron and magnesium to determine if their ratios may affect recoveries in the heaps.

We estimated that each fire assay for gold and silver costs $10.00 and each AA costs $5.00. Each bottle roll test costs $17.00. The laboratory cost $250,000 to construct and equip. All design, construction, and equipping was done by Zortman-Landusky Mining employees.

For 1983, it is estimated that our total mine costs will be $5.50/mt of ore or less than $10/gm of gold produced. Our production for 1983 is estimated to total 2,177 kg (70,000 oz) gold and 3,888 kg (125,000 oz) silver.

Chapter 4

AGGLOMERATED HEAP LEACHING AT ANACONDA'S DARWIN SILVER RECOVERY PROJECT

David A. Milligan
Phillip R. Engelhardt
Anaconda Minerals Company
P.O. Box 27007
Tucson, Arizona 85726

ABSTRACT

This paper outlines the research and development of a process to treat flotation tailings from the Darwin mill in Inyo County, California. A flowsheet was developed incorporating an agglomerated heap leach process using sodium cyanide to extract the silver values. Agglomeration was the key to developing this resource as the mill tailings averaged only 13% plus 100 mesh. Percolation through the heap would have been impossible without agglomeration to improve the permeability. The various tests that went into this research program are described with particular emphasis on the agglomeration techniques developed at the Anaconda Minerals Research Center. Start up and operation are discussed.

INTRODUCTION

This paper describes the Darwin Silver Recovery project, located 66 km (40 miles) outside of Lone Pine, near Darwin, Inyo County, California. A lead-zinc mine and a flotation concentrator were operated there from 1945 to 1957. By the time the mine was shut down, 1.53 Tg (1.69 million short tons) of tailings had been stored in ponds. An average silver assay of 47 mg/kg (1.38 troy oz/st) of tailings stimulated interest for commercial silver recovery.

A heap leach process was developed in 1981 at the Tucson Research Center of Anaconda Minerals Company, a division of Atlantic Richfield Company. Agglomeration techniques were used on the ore since the fine grind did not allow direct heap leaching. Lime and cement were required as binders. Early laboratory tests showed that recoveries equal to those from an agitated leach could be achieved at lower capital and operating costs. Laboratory tests determined cyanide requirements, lime and cement usages, and percolation or leach rates, as well as confirming that a zinc precipitation step could recover the silver from the leach solution.

The plant site requirements and the laboratory test data were used by an outside engineering firm to develop capital and operating cost estimates, to prepare process and engineering diagrams, and to construct the plant, which was started in the spring of 1982.

Personnel from the Tucson Research Center were involved in all phases of the preliminary test work, design, and construction, and were sent to the site to aid in start-up and with other problems that occurred.

Scope

Early work at the Tucson Research Center characterized the Darwin tailings with respect to grade, tonnage, and amenability. Representative samples were tested for silver recovery by cyanide leaching. These studies included mechanically agitated, vat, and heap leaches. Mechanically agitated leaches were studied on a laboratory, batch, and a continuous pilot plant scale; vat leaches were studied on a laboratory scale; heap leaches were studied in 5 and 10 kg (11 and 22 lb) laboratory columns, in 1,360 kg (3,000 lb) pilot plant columns, and in a 0.658 Gg (725 st) test heap. Other unit processes were studied, including crushing, grinding, liquid-solid separation, silver recovery, and cyanide destruction. The silver recovery tests included both carbon adsorption and zinc precipitation. The results of phases incorporated in the final plant design are included in this paper.

Darwin History

On August 1, 1945, The Anaconda Company purchased the Bernon, Defiance, Driver, Essex, Independence, Intermediate, Lane, Lucky Jim, Promontory, Rip Van Winkle, and Thompson mines, and other small properties in the Darwin, California, lead-silver-zinc district called the Darwin Hills. The location is shown in Figure 1. Anaconda consolidated the Bernon, Defiance, Essex, Independence, Intermediate, Rip Van Winkle, and Thompson mines, renamed them Darwin Mines, and started operation of the Darwin mill.

FIGURE 1
STATE OF CALIFORNIA

Anaconda operated the Darwin Mines and mill intermittently until 1957. The mill processed, in a sulfide circuit, 3.15 kg/s (300 stpd) of lead, zinc, and silver ore. In 1951, a 1.57 kg/s (150 stpd) oxide circuit was added to process lead oxide ore.

From 1945 through 1957, Anaconda produced approximately 12.4 kg (400 oz) of gold, 20.2 Mg (650,000 oz) of silver, 77 Mg (85 st) of copper, 6.1 Gg (6,700 st) of lead, and 2.7 Gg (3,000 st) of zinc yearly. Approximately 71.5 Mg (2.3 million oz) of silver were left in the tailings. The sulfide minerals consist principally of galena, sphalerite, and lesser amounts of pyrite, chalcopyrite, and pyrrhotite.[1] The average grade of ore in 1951 was 6 percent lead, 6 percent zinc, and 206 mg/kg (6 oz/st) of silver, with a small amount of copper. Gangue minerals are calcite, fluorite, and jasper. The relict host-rock minerals are garnet, idocrase, diopside, wollastonite, quartz, and feldspar. Jasper and calcite are abundant in most of the fissure deposits, and relict host-rock minerals occur in the replacement orebodies.

SUMMARY OF DARWIN OPERATIONS

The Darwin Silver Recovery Project was originated by the Anaconda tailings study team. By late 1980, a project team was assigned to the project. The original feasibility studies considered an agitated leach flowsheet with carbon-in-pulp (CIP). Heap leaching was not given serious consideration because of the very low intrinsic permeability of the tailings. In October of 1980, a sample of the tailings was agglomerated and leached in a laboratory column. Very favorable results were obtained. To further evaluate early testwork, extensive testing of agglomerates and heap leaching was begun at the Tucson Research Center. A pilot-scale test was also initiated using part of the old Yerington, Nevada, facility. The engineering contractor proceeded with the design of portions of the plant that were common to both an agitated leach and a heap leach.

During the same period of time, the project team defined two environmental problems--tailings storage and water availability. Storage of tailings as a slurry in a clay-lined pond was not acceptable to the State of California Water Quality Control Board, unless the residual cyanide was removed. Secondly, recalculation of the water requirement and a study of water availability gave evidence that the quantity of available water was one of the controlling factors in the plant design.

By early June, 1981, an agglomerated heap leaching flowsheet was adopted. This decision was based on both the favorable test results and the higher capital required for dewatering in a CIP flowsheet.

SILVER RESOURCES

Darwin tailings samples were submitted to the Tucson Research Center in three phases: (1) grab samples, (2) drill hole samples, and (3) bulk samples. The grab samples verify the existence of the silver prospect and its amenability. Five grab samples of Darwin tailings were received in June, 1980. They averaged 65 mg/kg (1.9 oz/st) of silver. The drill hole samples quantify the grades and tonnages and confirm the amenability. Sixty-two drill hole samples of Darwin tailings were received during 1980. Sample analysis and survey data indicated that the 1.53 Tg (1.69 million st) of Darwin tailings contain 47 mg/kg (1.38 oz/ton) of silver, with minor gold values.

These samples were to be studied for silver concentration and leach amenability. A mineralogy study indicated that silver is present in the form of micron- and submicron-sized grains of native silver, and naumannite (Ag_2Se) as inclusions in other minerals. There are probably low amounts of silver contained in other minerals (tetrahedrite, sphalerite, galena, chalcopyrite, pyrite, iron oxides and clays). Gold was also detected. Screen analyses run on various samples vary considerably, but average 13 percent +149 µm (100 Tyler sieve mesh) and 35 percent +74 µm (200 mesh).

Several sets of bulk samples were obtained during late 1980 and early 1981. These included samples for crusher, pilot plant agitated leach, filtration, pilot plant column leach, and large heap leach tests. From preliminary testing, a single bulk sample was selected for the Yerington, Nevada, test heap construction. To construct the heap, 0.658 Gg (725 st) was used. The sample used contained 55 mg/kg (1.6 oz/ton) of silver, 1.6 percent zinc, 0.94 percent lead, 0.06 percent copper, and 6.36 percent moisture.

PROCESS DEVELOPMENT

A standard series of amenability tests was conducted on the composite grab sample, including gravity separation and cyanide leach. Flotation and gravity separation resulted in low recoveries and a low-grade product; however, preliminary laboratory sodium cyanide leaches on Darwin tailings samples resulted in good extraction of the silver values.

Laboratory Agitated Leaching

Past experience has shown that laboratory mechanically agitated cyanide leaches produced silver extractions similar to those which can be obtained by operating agitated leach plants and provided the boundaries for heap and vat leaching. With the use of overhead stirrers, laboratory leaches were run in glass beakers by mixing a weighed tailings sample with a measured amount of water. A selected amount of lime (CaO) was added first, followed by the amount of sodium cyanide (NaCN) selected for that test. After the leach was finished, the slurry was filtered, the residue washed and dried, and the combined solutions and residue assayed. This procedure was performed on most of the Darwin tailings samples received.

The silver extraction results on the grab sample composite averaged above 72 percent on as-received material and above 75 percent on -74 µm (200 mesh) material. The extraction results for all drill hole samples averaged 70 percent as received. Similar results were obtained for pilot plant bulk samples. Sodium cyanide usage averaged 770 mg/kg (1.54 lb/st). This cyanide usage was based on 81 leaches.

Tests were run in which the amount of lime (CaO) added to the leach was varied to determine the optimum dosage for leaching. The results indicate that leaching with more lime than is necessary for protective alkalinity is beneficial for the extraction of the silver and reduces the sodium cyanide consumption. The tests were run on -150 µm (100 mesh) ore using three kg/m^3 (6 lb/st) of NaCN feed solution.

Heap Leach Testing

Originally, the Darwin tailings were thought to be unsuitable for heap leaching because of their inherent low permeability. The very high amount of fines present in the tailings (ore) from the old flotation plant tended to migrate and slow or stop the flow of solution through a heap. The process of agglomeration was an ideal method for preparing the Darwin tailings for heap leaching. Agglomeration with binders markedly increased the permeability and porosity of the ore and allowed a high flow of leach solution through the heap, while the fine particle size of the ore allowed fast, efficient leaching of the silver.

Heap leach testing began with column tests in the laboratory followed by larger column tests in the pilot plant. A large field test was also required. Several problems are encountered in modeling a heap leach operation using laboratory columns, pilot plant columns, or large field tests. The primary factors are lack of similarity of permeability, porosity, solution distribution, depth, ore size, and ore size segregation between the various tests and the actual field operations.

Laboratory Column. Laboratory leaches, using 0.61 m (2 ft) high and 0.14 m (5.5 in.) diameter plastic columns, were run after agglomerating the Darwin ore on a 0.4 m (16 in.) disk pelletizer. These tests were run on the tailings at -950 (3/8 in.), -630 (1/4 in.), -425 (35 mesh), and

-150 µm (100 mesh) grinds. The ore sample was mixed dry with lime and/or cement, and water was added on a pelletizer (rotating disk on an incline) to agglomerate and bind together the coarse and fine fractions of the ore. This mix was then charged to the column and allowed to cure. After three days, sodium cyanide solution was per-colated through the ore and collected. The flow rate and NaCN solution strength were varied in these tests.

The moisture content of the agglomerates used to pack the laboratory columns was 17 to 18 percent by weight. This was determined initially by observing the mix as it agglomerated on the pelletizer. The agglom-erates held up very well in the columns. After leaching and washing, the columns were allowed to drain for one day; they retained an average of 24 percent entrained moisture.

Laboratory column leach tests on agglomerated Darwin tailings gave good silver extractions (above 65 percent), with an average of 77 percent. Variables studied included agglomeration procedure, particle size, reagent addition (lime, cement, caustic and sodium cyanide), and leachant flow rate. The extraction of silver was best correlated to the leachant flow through the lab-oratory columns. Although flow rate was considered a very important variable, very little change was noted either in silver extraction or solution grade when equal volumes of leachant were contacted with the sample. Only when the flow in the 0.14 m (5.5 in.) column exceeded 33 mm^3/s (0.76 gpd) did significant bypassing of solution occur.

For cyanide leaching of silver to be effective, the pH must be controlled so that significant amounts of hydro-gen cyanide gas do not evolve from the heap. This control is normally gained by the addition of lime to the ore; however, an alternative is the addition of caustic soda. The initial grade of the silver in the solution with caustic soda was nearly twice that with lime. After 2 kg of solu-tion per kg of solids (2 st of solution per st of solids) had passed through the ore, the cumulative solution grade was increased only 15 percent. Silver extraction was also improved by approximately 10 percent. Although extrac-tion was increased, the added reagent cost was not justi-fied on this lower grade ore.

Pilot Plant Columns. Eight cyanide leach columns packed with agglomerated Darwin tailings were operated during the summer of 1981. The plant consisted of eight 0.92-meter-diameter (3 ft) by 1.22 meter-high (4 ft) clay tile leach columns run as individual units with approxi-mately 1-1/2-week leach cycles. On six of these columns, the pregnant solution accumulated, and the sil-ver and gold in the solution was periodically precipitated with zinc dust. The barren solution was recycled to the leach column. A flowsheet for these columns appears as Figure 2.

The pregnant solution from the remaining two columns circulated continuously through an activated carbon bed to adsorb the gold and silver. The resulting solution was then recycled to the leach column. A flow-sheet for these columns appears as Figure 3.

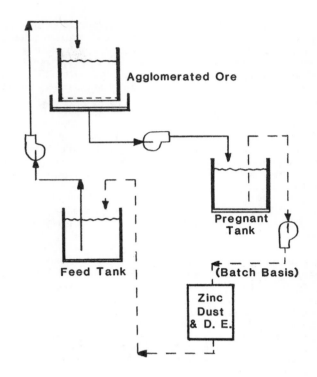

FIGURE 2

**DARWIN TAILINGS PILOT PLANT –
ZINC PRECIPITATION FLOWSHEET**

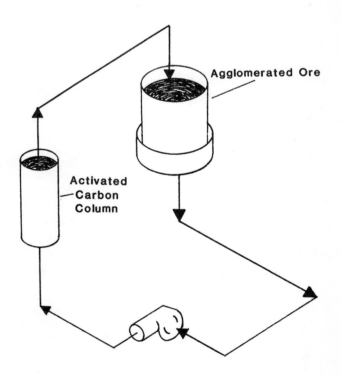

FIGURE 3

**DARWIN TAILINGS PILOT PLANT –
ACTIVATED CARBON FLOWSHEET**

The required reagents, sodium cyanide and sodium hydroxide, were added to the barren leach solution prior to its recycling onto the column. Sufficient cyanide was added to maintain 0.3 kg/m^3 (0.6 lb/st) of free cyanide; sufficient caustic was added to maintain solution pH above 10.0. The solution feed rate to the columns was set at 3.36 cm^3/s (77 gpd) of solution.

The material representing several sites from the tailings pond was agglomerated with lime, cement, and water in a modified cement mixer prior to being packed in the column. The proper moisture content was maintained by visual check and averaged 16.5 percent. Figure 4 illustrates the average cumulative extraction percentages and solution assays to be expected from a 0.92-meter-I.D. (3 ft) by 1.22-meter-high (4 ft) column packed with agglomerated Darwin tailings. The pilot plant used an average of one g/kg (2 lb/st) of sodium cyanide and 6 g/kg (12 lb/ton) of lime. The calculated pilot plant head sample assay was 54 mg/kg (1.58 oz/st) of silver. The extraction obtained in the pilot plant and laboratory averaged 72 percent and 63 percent, respectively (see Table 1).

TABLE 1

COMPARISON OF PILOT PLANT WITH 24-HOUR AGITATED LEACH

Column Number	Silver Assay of Ore		Silver Extraction [a]	
	mg/kg	oz/st	24hr leach (percent)	Pilot Plant (percent)
1	65.2	1.90	63.7	78.9
2	49.0	1.43	53.4	65.0
3	45.6	1.33	53.4	59.8
4	49.7	1.45	59.4	75.0
5	55.2	1.61	59.4	79.8
6	51.1	1.49	73.7	68.5
7	55.2	1.61	73.7	74.6
8	46.0	1.34	67.1	60.3

[a] Extraction percentage calculation based upon solution cutoff assay of 3 mg/kg (0.1 oz/st) of silver.

Test Heap. A 0.658 Gg (725 st) test heap was leached at Yerington, Nevada, during the summer of 1981. The heap was leached during three periods designated as Run I, Run II, and Training. Figure 5 illustrates the extraction performance of the test heap. The tailings were agglomerated in a modified trommel. Poor feed control resulted in an excessive addition of 17.5 g/kg (35 lb/ton) of lime and 21.5 g/kg (43 lb/ton) of cement. The agglomerated material was very stable below the top surface layer. The flowsheet for the Yerington, Nevada, heap leach operation is shown in Figure 6. The leach solution percolated through the agglomerated heap and was collected into a pregnant surge tank. The silver-containing solution was deaerated and contacted with zinc in a Merrill-Crowe zinc precipitator prior to its recycling as barren solution. The zinc precipitates were periodically removed. In the heap test the barren solution was typically below 0.1 mg/kg (0.003 oz/st) silver.

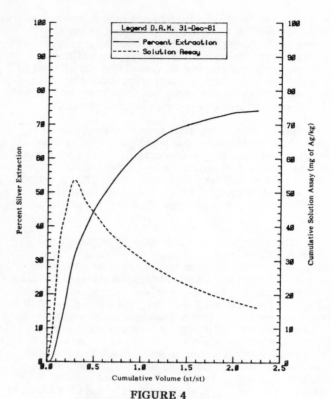

FIGURE 4

**DARWIN TAILINGS PILOT PLANT -
COLUMN AVERAGE RD-81-91**

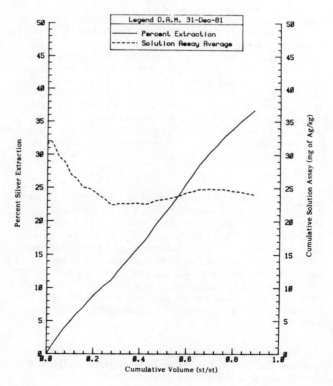

FIGURE 5

**DARWIN TAILINGS YERINGTON HEAP LEACH
EXTRACTION DATA FOR RUNS 1 AND 2, RD-81-91-2**

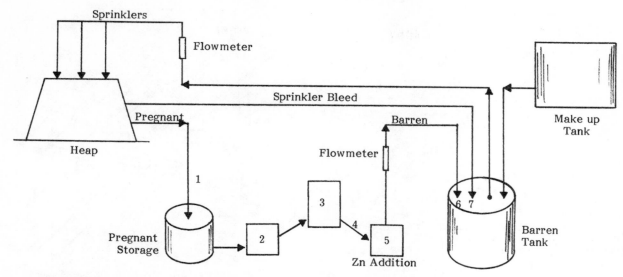

FIGURE 6

SCHEMATIC OF DARWIN HEAP LEACH PILOT PLANT
SHOWING SAMPLING AND READING POINTS

1. Pregnant flowrate + sample point
2. Clarification Fileter + pressure gauge
3. De-aeration unit + vacuum pump pressure gauge
4. Zn feed system
5. Precipitation filter + pressure gauge
6. Barren sample point
7. Sprinkler bleed flowrate

The test heap consumed a total of 0.89 g/kg (1.78 lb/st) of sodium cyanide. Approximately 0.25 g/kg (0.5 lb/st) was consumed during start-up and 0.025 g/kg (0.05 lb/st) of sodium cyanide per day was consumed during operation. The zinc consumption was 2.74 kg/kg (0.188 lb/oz) of silver for the first run, and 3.17 kg/kg (0.22 lb/oz) of silver for the second run. Combined zinc consumption was 2.92 kg/kg (0.20 lb/oz) of silver. Precipitate grade was low at 89 grams of precious metal per kilogram (2,600 oz/st) because of the excess of filter aid and zinc. Figure 5 illustrates silver extraction obtained.

Leach Comparisons. Leaching tests on one sample have included a 24-hour mechanically agitated leach, 10 kg (22 lb) laboratory column leach, 1,360 kg (3,000 lb) pilot plant column leach, and 0.658 Gg (725 st) test heap leach. Table 2 summarizes the results. Laboratory columns and pilot plant columns compare very well with the agitated leach results showing silver extractions between 70 and 75 percent. With a comparable amount of solution passed through the test heap, silver extractions were projected to be between 60 and 65 percent. The lower cumulative solution assay resulted from the solution bypassing the center portion of the heap.

DARWIN PLANT

By August, 1981, field construction had started utilizing an accelerated schedule commonly called the "fast track" concept. Design, procurement, plant construction, and obtaining permits proceeded concurrently through the balance of 1981. Figure 7 illustrates the Darwin flowsheet. The Waste Discharge Permit, sought from the Water Quality Control Board (WQCB), became the governing factor in the start-up of the plant. Anaconda made many changes in the design of the leach pad. Two of the most costly changes were (1) the addition of a third 0.15 m (6 in.) lift, and (2) the addition of 10 percent bentonite to the middle lift.

By late March, 1982, all necessary permits had been obtained and the first heap area was complete. When leach solution was applied, the agglomerate decrepitated, resulting in low percolation. An investigation suggested three changes in operation:

(1) More care used in making agglomerate.
(2) More cement added to make a durable agglomerate.
(3) Decreased heap height to prevent the loader from traveling on the toe of the previously deposited material.

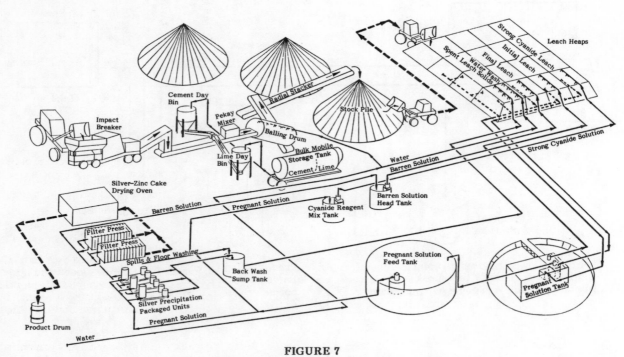

FIGURE 7

**ANACONDA MINERALS COMPANY
SILVER RECOVERY PLANT – DARWIN, CA.**

TABLE 2

LEACH COMPARISONS OF DARWIN SAMPLE RD 81-91-2

	Silver[a] Extraction(%)	Cum. Solution[a] Assay		NaCN[b] Addition		CaO[c] Addition	
		(mg/kg)	oz/st	g/kg	lb/st	g/kg	lb/st
24 hr mechanically agitated leach	73.7	19.9	0.58	0.4	0.8	1.9	3.8
10 kg (22 lb) laboratory column	70.5	19.1	0.56	0	0	16.8[e]	33.6[e]
1,360 kg (3,000 lb) pilot plant column	73.0	19.8	0.58	.75	1.5	5.6	11.2
0.658 Gg (725 st) test heap[d]	63.0	17.0	0.50	1.0	2.0	17[e]	35[e]

a   At 1.85 kg of total leach and wash solution per kg solids (1.85 st/st).
b   96% sodium cyanide.
c   100% available CaO – includes equivalent values of reagents used during agglomerations and leaching.
d   Projected from test heap data.
e   Excess amounts used.

After these changes the heap operated satisfactorily. Off-solution flow was clear, indicating no migration of fines. However, because of the hydrostatic head limitation on the clay pad which was stipulated in the waste discharge permit, solution application was restricted to twelve hours out of each twenty-four. This reduction in application rate doubled the leaching time, and operation continued through June.

The metal recovery section experienced minor difficulties with silver precipitation, and copper build-up in the circulation solution was thought to be causing the low efficiency in the zinc precipitation unit. Initially, higher levels of sodium cyanide were tried; however, the increased costs were high. Lead nitrate addition was found to be successful in increasing precipitation efficiency without significant cost increase.

At the end of June, 1982, after completing the first leach cycle, operation was suspended to excavate a portion of the pad and determine the depth of leach solution penetration. The pad investigation indicated solution penetration into the pad was much less than the design had predicted. Leaching was resumed in late July.

Agglomeration and heap construction changes solved the problem of low percolation. One change which added significantly to cost was the use of lower heap height. A new method of building 4.6 m (15 ft) high heaps was instituted during start-up in mid-July. The results were mixed. Problems with high solution levels above the pad continued; therefore, the solution application rate was frequently reduced.

Pad Construction

The leach pad was made of clay and constructed in three lifts. Each lift consisted of a 0.15 m (6 in.) compacted blend of soil and clay. The first lift was placed on a fairly even and relatively uniform sloped surface. The brush and 0.15 m (6 in.) of topsoil were removed to a stockpile for later reclamation of the heap area. The upper of 0.2 m (8 in.) soil was removed and stockpiled for use in constructing the second and third lifts.

The construction of the first lift began with spreading and mixing 0.05 m (2 in.) of clay with 0.10 m (4 in.) of soil. Once mixed with a disc, water was added as discing continued until a moisture of 15 to 17 percent was reached. Six passes of a vibrating roller completed the compaction. Moisture and compaction were monitored with a nuclear moisture density probe. The second lift contained an additional 0.013 m (1/2 in.) of bentonite, and the third lift was similar to the first. As the pad was built, the first lift was extended eighteen inches beyond the second lift, and the middle lift was extended beyond the top lift. This ensures that the pad seams do not overlap one another and that the pad will not fail at the seam.

When the third lift was complete, external and internal berms were constructed for solution control for the heap. The berms were used around the completed pad to prevent excursions of cyanide solution and to ensure that the solution reached the drain lines. Additional clay was used as berm material. Berm materials were made by mixing two parts clay with four parts soil, then adding water. The mixture was placed and compacted as needed.

The clay used in pad construction came from Black Springs Clay Company, Lone Pine, California. The bentonite was purchased from the Industrial Minerals Venture (IMV) plant located in the Nevada portion of the Amargosa Valley near the stateline.

The following equipment was used during construction of the pads:

Water truck - Modified Euclid R-50
Loader - either a Caterpillar 992 B or a
    Caterpillar 988 B
Dozer - Fiat-Allis 21C
Motor grader - Caterpillar No. 16
Tractor - S 530 TC Case Loader and Backhoe
Tractor - International 4586
Disc - Towner 5.5 m (18 ft)
Leveler-scraper - Model 15 CR w/dolly
Roller - Bros Vibratory VM 278

Mining

Mining of the tailings was controlled by minimizing haul distance and advance of the heap leach pad into mined areas. The agglomerator, although built on skids, would not be moved during the life of the project. The solution collection tank would be moved once. In the early operation, one 992 loader was required.

Dust generation in the traffic area was controlled by water sprays and a dust suppressant. Fine water mist sprays control dust in feeding, crushing, and agglomeration areas.

The material from the reclaim operation was charged to the receiving hopper by a 6- or 8-m³ (8 or 10 cubic yard) front-end loader. The operator controls plant throughput by observing and maintaining a nominal operating level in the ore-receiving hopper. Feed rate varied from 34 kg/s (135 stph) to 50 kg/s (200 stph). Material mined during 1982 averaged 45 mg/kg (1.31 oz/st) of silver with approximately 0.05 percent copper, 0.9 percent lead, and 1.3 percent zinc.

Agglomeration And Stacking

Optimization of agglomeration conditions is essential to optimize silver extraction and maximize solution silver content. The leachant must be uniformly distributed and flow quickly and evenly through the ore in the heap. To test the agglomerate strength an accelerated laboratory test was developed. The agglomerate was cured for six hours at 90°C (194°F), cooled, and dipped in water ten times. The fines generated indicated the agglomerate strength.

All laboratory data indicated that the heaps would be free-draining both during and after the leach period. The mechanically agitated leach data established the minimum binder at 3 g/kg (6 lb/st) of lime. This is required for pH control. The recommended start-up binder was 5 g/kg (10 lb/st) of lime and 7.5 g/kg (15 lb/st) of cement.

Agglomeration and stacking procedure (heap building) at Darwin each operated four 10-hour days per week with one day overlap. Agglomeration averaged 42 kg/s (165 stph) while heap building moved four-day cured material to the pads at over twice that rate. Feed rates to the agglomerate varied widely, resulting in poor control of the agglomerator.

At Darwin, the binder and ore were mixed using a modified in-line mixer prior to entering the agglomerating drum, where sufficient water was added to raise the moisture content to 15.7 percent. The agglomerate was stacked in a 6.35 Gg (7,000 st) curing pile. A front-end loader reclaimed the agglomerate from the curing pile for stacking on the pad. The heap was constructed of cells 46 by 38 meters (150 by 125 feet), built continuously without visible separation. The pad was designed to recover all of the solutions applied to and percolating through the leach dump into an underdrain system.

Permeability of the heaps at Darwin has not reached the heights attained at the Tucson Research Center, or the test heap at Weed Heights, Nevada. Problems occurred with both vertical and horizontal permeability in the first heap leach cell which contained approximately 5.4 Gg (6,000 st) of material. Low downward permeability restricted the solution application rate and increased leach time. The reduced vertical permeability appears to be the result of the low strength agglomerate. In order to improve agglomerate strength, the binder was changed from 5 g/kg (10 lb/st) of lime and 7.5 g/kg (15 lb/st) of cement to 17.5 g/kg (35 lb/st) of cement with no lime. The in-line mixer and agglomerator were also modified to obtain better mixing and higher retention time. The low horizontal permeability just above the pad created a flooded condition within the heap, restricting the rate of solution application even further. Some low permeability appeared to be the result of toe compaction by the front-end loader while stacking the heap. Solution recovery was improved by changing the underdrain design, by covering the drains with crushed rock, and by restricting toe compaction by the loader. Future operation envisions the use of a portable stacking conveyor to increase heap height, thus reducing pad cost and limiting compaction.

Heap Leaching

Cyanide heap leaching is an inexpensive method of extracting precious metal from ores. A dilute cyanide solution is applied to the surface of the heap (stacked ore). Percolation of the cyanide solution through the ore extracts the precious metal. The fine ore at Darwin leaches very quickly. The soluble silver and gold are extracted after approximately 3 kg of solution per kg of ore (3 st/st) has passed through the heap. Residual cyanide in the heap is then reduced by a fresh water wash.

The strong cyanide recycle and barren solutions, as well as the fresh water, flow in separate lines with a series of smaller plastic pipelines feeding the separated sprinkler systems. Twelve sprinklers on 3 m (10 ft) centers are installed on each line. The strong, barren, recycle, and wash solutions are applied until the required amount of solution per unit of agglomerate has been reached. Low permeability or permit head limitations lengthen the application time required. Solution advance maximizes solution grade.

Each of the cells has been sampled three times since termination of leaching to determine the silver extraction (see Figure 8). One-half of the heaps sampled yielded 72 percent silver extraction as predicted from laboratory and pilot plant operation. The ore in one-fourth of the heaps sampled yielded less than 25 percent silver extrac-

tion. The major reason for the low extraction in these heaps appears to be insufficient cyanide addition during the application of the strong cyanide solution. The remainder of the samples indicates that significant quantities of soluble silver were left in the heap. This metal loss resulted from reduced solution application and solution head limitations, both set by the California Water Quality Board. Approximately 11 percent of all silver originally in the ore was solubilized but not displaced from the heap as a result of the 35-day solution application limit.

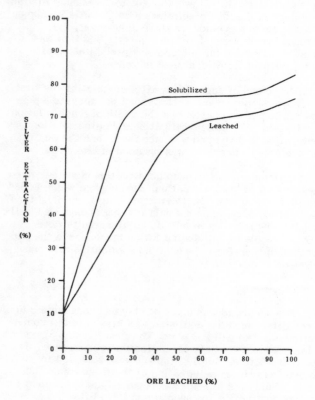

FIGURE 8

DARWIN HEAP LEACH PERFORMANCE

Solution Processing

Once the silver has been leached from the Darwin tailings it must be converted to a salable product. The precious-metal-bearing solution was treated by zinc dust precipitation and the barren solution was recycled to the leaching step. The average sodium cyanide makeup was 1.2 g/kg (2.4 lb/st) of ore. The pregnant solution, containing the silver and gold values was pumped to a pregnant solution storage/surge tank in the metal recovery area.

The precious metal recovery circuit used the conventional Merrill-Crowe process. The process included: (1) clarification and deaeration of the solution, (2) addition of metallic zinc for precipitation of silver and gold contained in the pregnant solution, and (3) filtration of the precious metal/zinc precipitate from the resultant barren solution. The barren solution, a dilute cyanide solution containing at least 0.3 kg/m^3 (0.6 lb/st) free cyanide, flows into a head tank, and then to the heaps for further dissolution of contained precious metal values after reagent adjustments have been made. Sodium cyanide pellets in 1360 kg (3,000 lb) capacity returnable bins discharge continuously into a strong cyanide mix tank for reagent makeup.

The precious metal/zinc precipitate in the filter was blown to a minimum moisture content with compressed air. The air-dried precipitate was removed from the filter and completely dried in an oven for direct shipment to a precious metal buyer. Future plans include the installation of a surplus induction furnace for smelting the precipitate to dore to reduce smelting and transportation costs.

Few problems with precious metal recovery were encountered in Darwin operations even though copper and cadmium tended to build up in the circulation solution. To the zinc was added 88 to 132 g/kg (0.088 to 0.132 lb/lb) of lead nitrate and 0.5 kg/kg (0.5 lb/lb) of filter aid. Zinc was fed as a slurry at 20 percent solids using peristaltic pumps. Effluent solution grades were maintained between 1 and 3 mg/kg (0.03 and 0.09 oz/st) of silver to minimize zinc consumption and to maximize zinc precipitate grades. The three modified skid-mounted Merrill-Crowe units were capable of handling a total of 9.5 dm^3/s (150 gpm).

Precipitate grades were orginally low because of the use of excess zinc and filter aid. Average precipitate grades of over 0.27 kg/kg (8,000 oz/st) of silver and 0.665 g/kg (19.4 oz/st) of gold were obtained. Precipitate grades near 0.58 kg/kg (17,000 oz st) were obtained during later operations.

Environmental Considerations

Environmental considerations played a significant part in the construction of the Darwin operation. The leach heap was placed on a 0.46 m (1-1/2 ft) thick clay pad with a coefficient of (hydraulic conductivity) one m/s (0.007 gpd/ft^2). The pad was surrounded by a clay lined collection ditch and sump to collect any run off, both shallow and deep monitoring wells were installed down dip, and topsoil was salvaged for use in covering the tailings after leaching. Six permits were necessary for the operation:

(1) Water Use (California Water Board)
(2) Waste Discharge (California Regional Water Quality Board)
(3) Air Quality (Great Basis Air Pollution Control District)
(4) Conditional Use (Inyo County)
(5) Operations Plan (Bureau of Land Management)
(6) Radioactive Material License (California Department of Health Services)

These permits each required a significant expenditure of manpower for obtaining, monitoring, and reporting, as well as imposing some restrictive operation conditions. The Waste Discharge permit has recently been revised to ease some of the operating constraints; i.e., increasing the allowable hydraulic head from 1-1/2 to 5 feet, and the leaching solution application time from 35 to 120 days.

Cyanide destruction by natural reaction with the ore, soil, clay, and microorganisms has been advanced as the major mechanism for returning the Darwin site to an environmentally safe condition. Treatment with chemicals is potentially possible at higher costs; however, with total containment, with very low precipitation, and with no potential for groundwater contamination, (there is no free ground water in the 52 m (170 ft) of alluvium) natural destruction is the preferred method of reducing cyanide content in the tailings. An extensive program of monitoring residual cyanide content of the heaps was started with the suspension of operation at Darwin. When cyanide solution contacts the Darwin tailings, approximately 0.25 g of sodium cyanide per kg (0.5 lb/st) of tailings is destroyed. Under conditions of heap leaching, about 0.025 g of sodium cyanide per kg (0.05 lb/st) of tailings is destroyed during each day of leaching. Under static conditions, the Yerington, Nevada, test heap had decreased in cyanide content from approximately 100 mg/kg (0.2 lb/st) of cyanide on June 30, 1981, to 10 mg/kg (0.02 lb/st) of cyanide on August 30, 1981. This represents a cyanide destruction rate of approximately 5 mg of sodium cyanide per kg (0.01 lb/st) of tailings per day. Detailed monitoring of the Darwin heaps started in January, 1983. At the present time, approximately 13.6 percent of the cyanide added to the Darwin circuit is present as soluble cyanide in the tailings. The cyanide is destroyed by a number of factors: (1) the ore may react with the cyanide forming cyano compounds, (2) the cyanide may be oxidized by contact with oxygen and sunlight, (3) bacteria may consume the cyanide, and (4) the cyanide may be converted to a gas and lost to the atmosphere. All of these factors contribute to the cyanide loss from the leaching circuit and assist in returning tailings to an environmentally acceptable condition.

Metallurgical Accounting

Metallurgical accounting at Darwin was disrupted by the shutdown and start-up, and by the short-term nature of the operation. Ore process rate and grade were determined by sampling and weighing on a belt going to the agglomerator. Overall silver production was determined from the weight and grade of the produced zinc precipitates. This information, along with the reagent consumption data, was accumulated on a monthly basis.

On a daily basis, samples of feed, agglomerate, Merrill-Crowe feed, and barren solution were composited along with solution flows for daily control procedures. Water usages were determined weekly. The barren solution was sampled and assayed several times each shift by the operator for control of zinc addition to the Merrill-Crowe process.

REFERENCES

1. W. H. Hall and E. M. MacKevett, Jr., "Geology and Ore Deposits of the Darwin Quadrangle, Inyo County, California," USGS Geological Survey Professional Paper 368, 1963.

Chapter 5

PILOT SCALE HEAP LEACHING AT THE PINSON MINE, HUMBOLDT COUNTY, NEVADA

Mark E. Smith
W. B. Craft
Pinson Mining Company
P.O. Box 192
Winnemucca, Nevada 89445

ABSTRACT

To allow recovery of gold values from ore which cannot be economically processed by the mill, Pinson Mining Company has developed a run-of-mine heap leaching facility. In order to estimate production scale recovery rates, reagent consumption and percolation problems, a series of pilot scale tests were performed. These tests typically consisted of 3,630 metric tons (mt) (4,000 tons) leach ore at a grade of .94 to 1.56 grams Au per metric ton (g/mt) (.03 to .05 oz. Au/ton). Test heaps were loader stacked to approximately 4.3 meters (14 feet) high.

Information from these pilot scale tests was employed in the design and construction of the production scale facility. Parameters such as spray rate, leach cycle, sprinkler placement, and barren solution chemistry were determined by the pilot tests.

INTRODUCTION

The Pinson orebody is a finely disseminated, well-oxidized hydrothermal deposit. Gold particles are primarily finer than 20-microns and are typically less than 5-microns. The ore is silicified jasperoid and shale, with the higher grades associated with higher silicification and alteration. Sulfides and carbonaceous materials are negligible, some arsenic and mercury along with minimal amounts of silver are present.

Construction of the plant facilities and mining began in mid-1980. Mill production started in early 1981 and the first bullion was poured in February 1981.

Approximately 1,360 metric tons per day (mtpd) (1,500 tons per day) at .10 ounces per ton gold are milled while an additional 1,360 mtpd (1,500 TPD) at .025 are heap leached. Remaining reserves of 3 million tons mill ore and 2.2 million mt (2.4 million tons) leach ore have been identified. Mill recoveries to date are about 86% of total gold.

The Pinson project produces about 1,710 kilograms (55,000 ounces) gold per year, or 5% of total domestic production. Small amounts of silver and mercury are also produced as biproducts.

The project is located in northcentral Nevada, 38 miles northeast of Winnemucca by road, or about 320 km (kilometers) (200 miles) northeast of Reno. The orebody is situated along the eastern flank of the Osgood Mountains, primarily along the contact of an Ordovician limestone (Comus formation) and a Cambrian shale (Preble formation).

Heap leaching of the lower grade material (.01 to .04 ounces per ton) began in late 1982 and will continue through the life of the mine. Run-of-mine size (36" by clay) leach ore is stacked on 90 meters (300 feet) square clay leach pads, and put under leach for 60 to 90 day periods. After completion of the primary leach cycle, heaps will be releached on approximately 12 month cycles. Recovery rates to date are in the 50 to 60 percent range. Several stacking methods and heap heights are presently being evaluated to determine the optimum combination.

MILL:

The mill circuit consists of two stage ball mill grinding with carbon absorption columns for pregnant thickener overflow solution and a CIP circuit following the agitated leach of the thickener underflow pulp. Pinson was the first gold operation to use carbon columns and CIPs to recover values from solution.

Ore from the coarse ore stockpile is fed to the crushing plant hopper by a Cat 980 or 966 loader. Primary reduction is achieved through a 107 x 122 cm (42" x 48") jaw followed by a 1.7 m (5½') cone crusher in a closed loop configuration. Minus 1.3 cm (minus 1/2") ore is fed to a 1,540 mt (1,700 ton) capacity fine ore bin.

Mill feed is withdrawn from the fine ore bin by two long slot belt feeders. Dry cyanide and pebble lime are fed on the mill feed belt with the ore to the primary Kennedy Van Saun (KVS) 2.7 x 4.0 m (9' x 13') ball mill. An Allis-Chalmers (AC) 3.7 x 4.3 m (12' x 14') ball mill provides the finishing grind. Both mills discharge into a common sump feeding a bank of six Krebs 15" cyclones for classification; cyclone underflow is returned to the AC mill while the overflow passes through a DSM screen before going to the thickener. The grind at Pinson is held at 10 to 20% plus 200 Tyler mesh as coarser grinds do not provide sufficient liberation for acceptable leach extractions.

The cyclone overflow is thickened to 40% solids in a 100' diameter uncovered flat bottomed thickener with a conventional Eimco mechanism. The thickener overflow is pumped to a headbox feeding five 1.5 x 3.7 meter (5' x 12') upflow carbon absorption columns. The columns each contain 1 ton of 6 x 12 mesh activated coconut shell carbon which absorbs the gold cyanide complex from solution. The barren solution from the columns is returned to the grinding sump. The carbon in the columns is advanced counter-current every other day by water eduction.

The thickener underflow is leached in four steel agitator tanks located outdoors. From the leach/agitator tanks the pulp is fed into the mill where the gold is recovered in five 3.4 x 7.0 m (11' x 23') carbon-in-pulp (CIP) tanks. Each CIP tank contains .9 to 1.4 mt (1 to 1½ tons) of 6 x 12 mesh carbon. The carbon is

advanced counter-current every other day using
a recessed impeller centrifugal pump. Discharge
from the CIP circuit is screened on a 28 mesh
deck, to recover fine carbon and spills, and
then pumped to a clay lined tailings impoundment.

MINE:

The Pinson orebody is a Carlin type deposit,
formed in a shallow hot springs environment.
Alteration and mineralization are associated
with a granodiorite intrusive of Cretaceous age.
High gold-to-silver ratios are typical. Mercury
content varies from nil to 10 times the gold
content. Sulfides are absent and there is
virtually no preg. robbing carbonaceous material
in Pinson ore. Some silica encapsulation of
the fine gold particles is present, particularly
in the higher grade (and highly silicified) ore.
This gold is not completely liberated even at a
minus 400 Tyler mesh grind.

Mining of the Pinson orebody is being done in
two stage pits, each corresponding to one of the
two primary ore zones, the A-zone and the B-zone.
A north-east trending extension of the A-zone
has been identified, and exploration is continu-
ing in that area. Total remaining reserves at
Pinson of 2.7 million mt (3 million tons) mill
feed at 2.904 g/mt (.093) and 2.2 million mt
(2.4 million tons) leach ore at .812 g/mt (.026
ounces per ton) have been proven.

A-zone ore is a red, silicified matrix (locally
called a jasperoid) primarily along the contact
of the Cumus limestone (Ordovician) and the
Preble shale (Cambrian) formations. This
jasperoid is extremely hard with a Bond index
averaging 17. Grade drops off rapidly in the
limestone and shale. B-zone mineralization is
not bounded by definite hanging and foot walls.
Less silicification is present and the ore is
typically softer than A-zone ore. Although
B-zone material is primarily shale, less clay
is present than in the A-zone and therefore
this material is more amenable to heap leaching.

Primary drilling at Pinson is done with Reed
equipment. Two truck mounted SK-35's and a
crawler mounted SK-40 drill 6-3/4 inch diameter
blast holes 7.3 m (24 feet) deep in either
3.7 x 3.7 m (12 x 12 ft.) or 4.3 x 4.3 m (14 x
14 ft.) patterns. Cuttings from the holes are
assayed for grade control.

Ore is loaded with a Cat 992 front-end loader
equipped with a 9 cubic meter (12 cubic yard)
bucket or a Liebherr 982 hydraulic shovel employ-
ing a 4 cubic meter (5½ cubic yard) dipper. The
haulage fleet consists of five Wabco and two
Caterpillar 45 mt (50 ton) haul trucks. The
ore is hauled nearly 1.6 Km (one mile) to a
stockpile at the mill while the waste is hauled
1.1 Km (two-thirds of a mile) to dumps situated
south and east of the pit. Leach grade material
is hauled approximately 1.6 Km (one mile) to the
production heaps and placed directly on the pads.

A second orebody located 24 Km (15 miles) south
of the Pinson mine, referred to as the Preble
deposit, is presently under development. The
Preble ore is primarily shale, ranging from
severely weathered and clayey to hard, silicified
material. Mining of this deposit is scheduled
to commence in the near future, and the ore will
be processed by heap leaching.

PILOT HEAP LEACH TESTING

Heap leach pilot scale testing at Pinson started
in late summer of 1981. To date a total of five
tests on run-of-mine size ore have been completed.
Each test consisted of approximately 4,100 mt
(4,500 tons) of leach ore ranging in grade from
.94 to 1.87 g/mt (.03 to .06 ounces per ton)
stacked with a Cat 992 loader to approximately
4.3 m (14-feet high). Tests on A-zone, B-zone,
a blend of both ores, and Preble ore have been
completed, and a second test on Preble ore was
underway as of this writing. Parameters used in
the design of the production facility, such as
spray rate, leach cycle, sprinkler placement,
and barren solution chemistry were determined by
the pilot tests. Crushed and agglomerated tests
on Preble ore and A-zone ore are planned for
later this year.

The test facility consists of a 35 m (115')
square asphaltic pad 18 cm (7-inches) thick, two
solution ponds, 170 cu.m. preg. and 114 cu.m.
barren (45,000 gallon and 30,000 gallons,) a set
of three 36 cm (14-inch) diameter carbon columns,
and associated piping and pumps. Both ponds are
lined with 30 mil CPE plastic membranes. CPE
was chosen for its superior weathering characteristics as compared to PVC, and its economics as
compared to Hypalon. Spray solution is pumped
from the barren pond to the heap. Solution is
distributed through 5.1 cm (2") Yelomine PVC
pipe and sprayed by No. 10 Senninger wobblers and
.3 cm (1/8 inch) wigglers. The wobblers have
performed well and are presently being used in
the production facility. The wigglers require
much maintenance and will not be used on production heaps, but are required on the smaller test
heaps to give full solution coverage without
significant overspray.

Wobblers and wigglers produced large droplets,
and thus low evaporation and wind losses result.
Net solution losses for the pilot tests range
from 10 to 20% of total solution applied.
Solution loss is an economic loss because of
pumping costs and reagents and gold contained
in solution which is blown away. Additionally,
both types of sprays require only .10 MPa (Mega
Pascals) (15 psi) to operate, as compared to .3
to .4 MPa (40 to 60 psi) for impulse type spray
heads. This results in lower pumping costs and
lower pressure piping.

Pregnant solution is returned from the test pad
through a 7.6 cm (3-inch) high density
polyethelene pipe, and is stored in the preg
pond. Solution is pumped through the carbon
columns at the rate of .0013 to .0016 cubic

meters per second (cu.m/s) (20 to 25 gpm), where gold is loaded onto 6 x 16 mesh coconut shell carbon. Carbon advancing is determined by barren solution grade. After flowing through the carbon columns the solution is returned to the barren pond where cyanide, caustic soda and mill reclaim water are added. No fresh water is added to the test circuit. Reagents are added batch wise to a distribution box where the barren solution enters the spray pond.

Barren solution is applied at a rate of .17 cu. m/day/sq.m. (.003 gpm/square foot). Cyanide is maintained at about .50 kg/mt (1 pound/ton) and pH between 10 and 11. An antiscalant compound is added to the spray solution at the rate of 10 ppm to prevent scaling of the piping, spray heads and heap.

Several variations of the test conditions were made. On-off cycling of the sprays was tested several times. Typically the sprays would be operated one or two shifts, then shut off for one shift. Daily gold recoveries indicate that full-time or near full-time leaching provides maximum recovery rate.

Spray rate has been varied over a wide range, from .08 to .23 cubic meters per day per square meter (cu m/d/sq m) (.0015 to .0040 gpm/square foot). The optimum flow rate appears to be about .17 cu m/d/sq m (.003 gpm/square foot). Above this flow dilution of the solution and run off occurs, while below this inadequate leaching takes place.

Addition of hydrogen peroxide into the barren stream was tested as an aid to oxidation of the ore. Peroxide was added at the rate of 1200 ppm of 35% solution. No apparent effect on solution grade or recovery rate was observed, but a significant reduction in cyanide consumption and stabilization of pH resulted.

Of the four tests which have been completed on Pinson ore, recoveries of 66 to 82% have been achieved in 50 days, with an average of about 73%. Tests were performed on A-zone, B-zone, and a blend of both ore types. The blended ore exhibited the best recovery while the B-zone the lowest.

Three stacking methods were employed for the five pilot tests. The first A-zone test was stacked in a 5 m. (15-feet) high lift by driving trucks up a ramp and back dumping the ore. This test exhibited poor percolation and a low recovery rate. The next three Pinson tests and the first Preble test were stacked to about 5 m. (15-feet) high with a rubber-tired loader. The top of the heap was subsequently leveled with a Cat D-6 dozer. The loader stacked Pinson heaps exhibited excellent percolation with high recovery rates, while the Preble test showed poor percolation. The second Preble test was also loader stacked but the top was not worked with any equipment. Preble ore is very soft and clayey and is easily broken down by heavy equipment. The surface of

the first heap was severely degradated and compacted by the dozer work, while the second heap was left undisturbed. Although the second heap also exhibited poor percolation, this was somewhat mitigated by the undisturbed surface. The solution penetrated the ore more uniformly than for the first Preble heap with the disturbed surface.

TEST RESULTS - PINSON ORE:

Of the tests on Pinson ore, the blended A-zone/ B-zone test is probably most representative of actual production conditions. Although ore is not blended intentionally, production heaps are stacked with ore as mined directly from the two stage pits, and thus are composed of small pockets of each ore type.

The blended ore test consisted of 3,180 mt (4,054 tons) of A-zone/B-zone (33%/67%), blended by constructing a stockpile in several five foot thick lifts. The test heap was constructed by unloading the stockpile and stacking the heap with a rubber-tired loader, to an average height of about 4.3 m (14 feet). Spray solution was applied via eleven wobblers and twenty-six wigglers along the slopes. Head samples were taken during loading of the heap by sampling 22 to 44 Kg (10 to 20 pounds) of material out of every dumped bucket load. This procedure was repeated during unloading to provide a double check on the head grade. The grade of the blended ore was established at 1.19 g/mt (.038 oz./ton) gold (by fire assay).

The heap was put under leach during August and September of 1982. After eleven days of continuous leaching the spray period reduced to 16 hours per day for a seven day period to determine the effect on recovery rate. A slight reduction in the daily gold recovery was evidenced, however this was, at least partially, offset by reduced evaporation and wind losses.

Fourteen days after the resumption of continuous leaching, hydrogen peroxide was added to the spray solution at the rate of 1200 ppm of 35% solution. The purpose of peroxide addition is to aid in oxidation, which is essential to the gold cyanide reaction. Should any portion of the heap be deficient in oxygen, incomplete leaching would result.

Preg solution grade and recovery rate were not affected by the peroxide addition. However, a noticeable reduction in cyanide consumption and increased preg solution pH resulted. The reduced cyanide consumption is probably due to conversion of cyanide complexes to free cyanide, or neutralizing cyanide consuming agents in the ore. The cost of peroxide addition was not offset by the reduced cyanide and caustic soda consumption, and therefore its use was discontinued. Subsequent laboratory and mill scale tests confirmed no effect on recovery, but not the reduced reagent consumption.

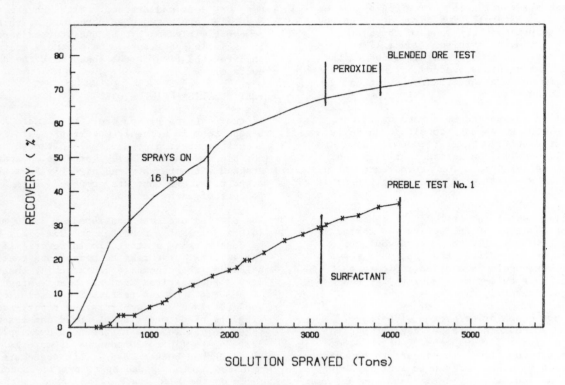

Figure 1. Gold Recovery Curves for Preble Ore and
Blended Pinson Ore.

This test ran a total of 41 days, and yielded 76% of total contined gold (by fire assay). The feed grade checked well with the tail grade. Sodium cyanide and sodium hydroxide consumptions of 1.6 and .73 Kg/mt (0.66 and 0.30 pounds per ton) ore respectively, and solution evaporation and wind losses of 19% were observed.

The test was terminated while the recovery curve was still rising and preg solution grade was at a high enough level to operate profitably on a production scale. It is interesting to note that 80% of the ultimate recovery was achieved in only 25 days. This is a relatively quick response for silicified run-of-mine ore, and has been confirmed by the other ROM tests. This phenomenon has both positive and negative effects. The fast initial leaching means the "cream" can be skimmed from recently stacked ore, returning the investment in a shorter period. However, this also results in tremendous spikes in the daily recovery, which can cause bottlenecks in the recovery circuit (carbon columns and electrowinning cell).

As previously mentioned, a scale inhibitor is used in the heap leach circuit, although no treatment has been required in the mill circuit.

The long contact time between solution and ore allowed by heap leaching, plus the various changes in solution chemistry through the circuit (temperature gradients, aeration) amplify the effect of scaling.

The A-zone ROM test began with inadequate scale treatment and severe scaling of the pumps, flow meters, spray heads and the heap surface resulted. During the eleven day period prior to supplying adequate protection, 9% downtime was suffered due to scaling, and near blinding of the heap resulted. Pick and shovel work was required on top of the heap to break up the scale layer. With addition of an acceptable antiscaling compound virtually no scaling occurred during the rest of the test.

A releach cycle was tried on the A-zone test. After the primary leaching for 53 days the heap was allowed to "rest" for four months then releached for one week. During this period an additional recovery of 3% was achieved, which is approximately five times the rate at the end of the primary cycle.

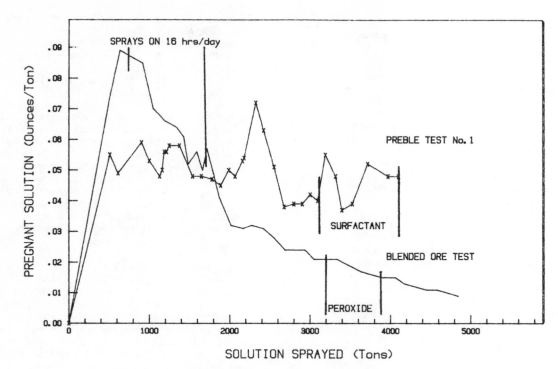

Figure 2. Gold Concentration in the Pregnant Solution from the Leaching of Preble Ore and Blended Pinson Ore.

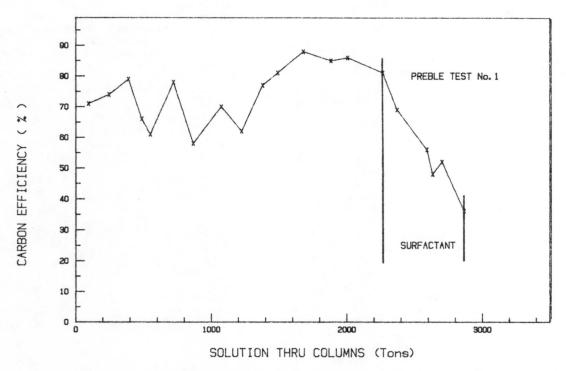

Figure 3. Carbon Loading Efficiency for Gold from the Preble Test.

TEST RESULTS - PREBLE ORE:

The Preble tests have been run-of-mine size ore
(18" x clay) exposed by a small stage pit on the
property. The first test was on near surface,
highly weathered ore. This material proved to
be very clayey and immediately showed
percolation problems when solution was added to
the heap after loader stacking. The percolation
problem was mainly responsible for keeping
operating time to 55% in the 65 day test period.
(A nonionic, ethylene/propylene oxide based
surfactant was tested as an aid to percolation.
It was added at a rate of 200 ppm for the final
2 weeks of the test. No obvious effect in
recovery rate, percolation, or reagent
consumption was observed during its use, however
the carbon efficiency dropped drastically after
treatment began. Due to the adverse effect on
the carbon the use of the surfactant has been
discontinued and no further testing is planned.)

A recovery of nearly 40% was obtained in the
first Preble test. Even though this was low,
several significant factors were brought out.
The preg solution grade was still over .94 g/mt
(0.03 oz./ton) when the test was halted; the low
recovery after 65 days was a result of the
reduced percolation rate. This indicated that
Preble ore is quite amenable to cyanide leaching.
During unloading of the heap no evidence of
channeling was observed. The percolation problem
in the first test was thought to be due to a
high clay fraction caused from weathering;
therefore, it was decided to halt the first test
and start a second test on deeper Preble ore.

The second ROM test on Preble ore, from a deeper
and less weathered portion of the orebody
(approximately 40-feet below the surface) was
underway as of this writing.

FULL SCALE EXPERIENCE

The first production heap was put on line in
December, 1982. This heap consisted of about
54,500 mt (60,000 tons) of blended Pinson ore
stacked to an average height of 6 m (20 feet).
Heap construction was achieved by building a
ramp 7.6 m (25 feet) high, delivering the ore to
the crest of the heap with haul trucks and
pushing over the sides with Cat D-8 dozers. Upon
completion of ore haulage, the upper 1.5 m (5
feet) of material was pushed off to the side of
the heap. The surface was ripped to about 1.2 m
(4 feet) deep prior to placing the spray piping.
Leaching of this ore took place primarily in
January and February under continuous sub-freezing
conditions. Approximately 50% availability was
achieved with no provisions made to mitigate
freezing other than discontinuing the sprays
whenever 2 cm (3/4 inch) of ice built up on
the heap, allowing the ice to melt in the
sunlight before resuming spraying. During this
two month leach cycle 53% recovery of total

contained gold was achieved. Poor percolation
was noted during the last four weeks of
leaching, with 30 to 40% of the spray solution
running off the sides. This percolation problem
was attributed to shallow compaction of the ore,
aggravated by migration of the clayey fraction
of the material. Subsequent ripping of the heap
confirmed this conclusion.

Due to the discrepancy between pilot and
production heaps, the decision was made to test
several alternate heap stacking methods. The
second heap was stacked to a final height of
7.6 m (25 feet) using a similar method as the
first, with the exception that truck traffic was
restricted to a 15 m (50 feet) wide road at the
center of the heap. Ore was pushed up to 46 m
(150 feet) with dozers. This heap yielded 59%
recovery of contained gold values after 65 days
of near continuous leaching.

Loader stacking to 4.3 m (14 feet) high was
employed for the third heap, which was under
leach as of this writing. After only two weeks
under sprays over 60% recovery had been achieved.
It is interesting to note that this ore is the
lowest grade of the three, .87 g/mt (.028 oz /T)
compared to 1.03 and 1.12 g/mt (.033 and .036
oz /T) for the first and second heaps,
respectively.

These three heaps serve to demonstrate the
sensitivity to stacking method the Pinson ore
demonstrates. This ore is very clayey and
subject to compaction, fines migration and
segregation of the coarser fractions.
Excellent recoveries were achieved from the
pilot tests without crushing, and percolation
problems can be mitigated without agglomeration
or other pretreatment.

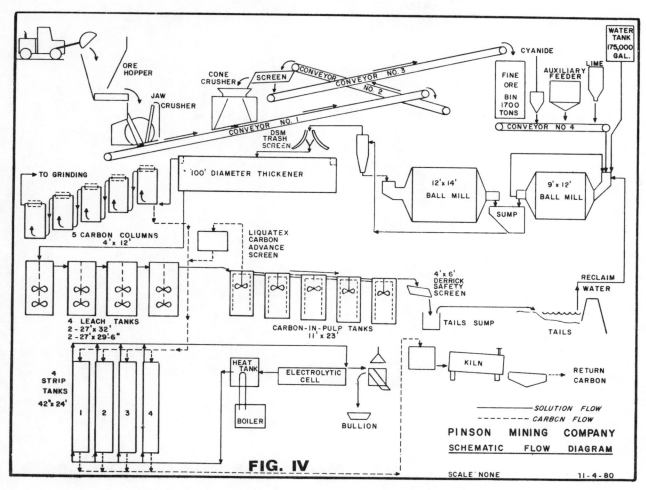

Figure 4. Schematic Flow Diagram for the Pinson Mill Circuit.

Chapter 6

GETTY MINING COMPANY'S
APPROACH TO HEAP LEACHING AT THE MERCUR MINE

Kendall Y. Keuhey
William E. Coughlin
Getty Mining Company
P.O. Box 838
Tooele, Utah 84074

ABSTRACT

The Mercur Mine, developed and operated by Getty Mining Company, is designed to process 3,000 tons/day of gold ore from the historic Mercur Hill mining district. The mill process involves crushing, grinding, and cyanide carbon-in-leach for recovery of gold from ores ranging from 0.08 to 0.10 oz/ton.

During the mining of normal grade ore, a substantial tonnage of material containing 0.02 to 0.05 oz/ton is mined and would be available for heap leaching. Also, Getty Mining is developing methods to test and prepare lower grade material for heap leaching by rejecting a coarse rock fraction from the grinding SAG mill circuit. This lower grade fraction is suitable for heap leaching, and its removal will upgrade the regular mill feed.

Other test methods are directed toward leaching techniques on some 4.0 million tons of tailings that resulted from roasting and/or cyanide leaching Mercur ores in the early 1900's.

The natural carbons associated with the Mercur deposits require special treatment to reduce their gold adsorption effects when leached with cyanide.

INTRODUCTION

The Mercur Gold Mine of Getty Minerals Company is a newly developed open pit mine located 65 miles southwest of Salt Lake City in the historic Mercur Mining District. Gold had been mined at Mercur from the 1890s to 1942 by underground mining methods.

MINE DESCRIPTION

The gold at Mercur occurred as micron-size particles that were deposited in the carbonate host rocks from hydrothermal solutions in a hot spring environment. Minerals associated with the gold are pyrite, marcasite, orpiment, realgar, barite, and remobilized carbon.

MILL DESCRIPTION

The as-designed plant at Mercur calls for milling 2,721.6 tons per day (3,000 st per day) or 3.086 g/mt (.09 oz/st) of gold ore by crushing it to -20.32 cm (-8 inches), then grinding it in an open circuit sag mill followed by a closed circuit ball mill, and then followed by a carbon-in-leach circuit. It was suspected at first and proven later that if the larger material could be removed from the sag mill, the feed to the leach circuit would be upgraded without a significant decrease in the number of total ounces of gold in the leach feed.

HEAP LEACHING AT MERCUR

With three different types of potential heap leach feed, sub-ore from the mine, sag mill rejects from the mill, and old mill tailings from the past mining operations, Getty decided to investigate heap leaching as a possible companion process to the milling operation.

METHODS: Heap leach testing was done two ways. A 453.6 kg (1,000 lb) barrel test or 181.44 mt (200 st) pilot heap leach was used.

BARREL TEST: The barrel tests were done in 378.5 l (100-gallon) polyethelene tanks. The distribution system for the leach solution was a "T" of 1.27 cm (1/2") PVC pipe connected to a variable speed DC gear motor that was rotated slowly to insure an even distribution over the ore in the barrel. A 5.08 cm (2") layer of clean gravel was put on the bottom of each barrel to allow the solution to reach the drain hole in the side of the barrel after percolating through the ore. The leach solution feed to the test barrels was from a constant level head tank and was controlled at each test barrel by pinch clamps. The discharge from the barrels (pregnant solution) was collected in 113-liter (30-gallon) polyethelene tanks.

Each day the volume of pregnant solution was measured and samples taken to determine gold and cyanide content and pH. The solution was then

transferred to the strip tank where it was pumped through a carbon column until the gold content was below .0171 gm/mt (.0005 oz/st). The stripped solution was then recycled to the constant head tank to be reused as leach solution. (See Fig. 1)

At the end of each test the barrels were dumped, the ore was air dried, and a tail sample was split out.

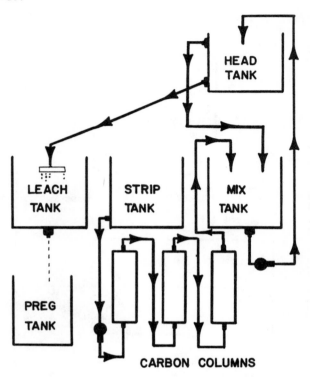

FIGURE 1. BARREL HEAP EQUIPMENT LAYOUT

HEAP PAD: The other testing procedure was done on a larger scale. The heap leach pad itself was 22.88 m x 24.4 m (75' x 80'), constructed of a 20-mill PVC lining material. The lining material was put down over a compacted bed of 15.24 cm (6") of sand. The heap itself was roughly 9.61 m (31.5') square with a 1:1 slope, being 1.83 m (6') at the highest point with a 5.95 m (19.5') square top. There was 15.24 cm (6") of compacted sand put down between the heap pile and the lining.

The pregnant solution pond was 6.10 m x 13.42 m (20' x 44') and was 1.22 m (4') in depth. The pond was able to contain a total of 43,531.2 l (11,500 gal) of pregnant liquor.

The heap pile was sprayed with barren solution at a rate of .122 l pm/sq m (.003 gpm/sq') using one #14 Senninger wobbler. The Senninger wobbler was chosen for the coarse droplet size to minimize both evaporation and wind drift. The pregnant solution draining from the heap would flow into the pregnant pond. The solution was then pumped out of the pond by a 1/5 hp pump into a 378.53 l (100-gal) polyethelene retaining tank. From the retaining tank, a 1-hp pump was used to pump the solution through three 12.7 cm (5") plastic carbon columns in series. (See Figure 2) The three 12.7 cm (5") columns were able to give enough room for the 50-100% carbon expansion needed for efficient carbon loading. The solution leaving the carbon columns first went through a flow meter to record the volume of solution put onto the pad.

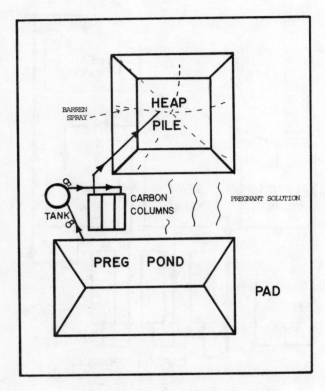

FIGURE 2. LEACH PAD EQUIPMENT LAYOUT

MERCUR SUB-ORE

ORE PREPARATION: The initial sample was taken from the Mercur ore stockpile from an area believed to be a low grade ore. The sample was then air dried and crushed down to -2.54 cm (-1"). The sample was split down to obtain a head sample. Next the ore was loaded by batches into a cement mixer where the ore was agglomerated with a 9.07 kg/mt (20 lb/st) cyanide solution. The sample was then weighed and loaded into a 378.53 l (100-gal) polyethelene tank that had a 5.08 cm (2") layer of washed gravel put in the bottom of the tank for filtering. The ore was then cured for 24 hours.

PROCEDURE: The equipment layout was used as stated in the preceding barrel test method. A 1kg/mt (2 lb/st) of cyanide solution was sprinkled by revolving sprinkler arms at the average rate of .015 l/min (.004 gpm) per .093 sq m (sq ft). The pH level was maintained at 10.4-10.7.

RESULTS: A total of 60.34% of the contained gold was extracted in 16 days of leaching. (See Graph 1)

Total cyanide consumption was 1.043 kg/mt (2.3 lb/st) for this test.

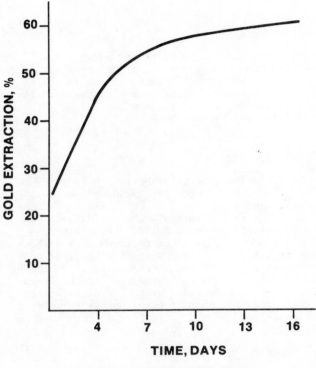

GRAPH 1. SUB-ORE BARREL

OXIDE-AGGLOMERATED WITH CEMENT VS. NO CEMENT

ORE PREPARATION: The sample was taken from the Mercur ore stockpile in an area believed to be low grade oxide ore. The ore was crushed to -2.54 cm (-1"), and the sample was split to make two separate samples. One split was then agglomerated with a 1% cyanide solution.

The second split was also agglomerated with a 1% cyanide solution and Portland Type II cement in the ration of 9.072 kg/t (20 lb/st). Both samples were then weighed and put into the leach tank to cure for 24 hours.

PROCEDURE: The equipment layout was used as stated in the preceding barrel test method. A 1kg/mt (2 lb/st) of cyanide solution was sprinkled by revolving sprinkler arms at the rate of .015 l/min (.004 gpm) per .093 sq m (sq ft). The pH level was maintained at 11.8.

RESULTS: Agglomerating the ore with cement in this case did not aid in the recovery of gold.

An extraction of 78.1% of the contained gold was achieved in 32 days of leaching with the ore that was not agglomerated with cement. The ore that was agglomerated with cement had an extraction of only 70.2% in 32 days of leaching. (See Graph 2)

A cyanide consumption of .463 kg of NaCN/mt (1.02 lb/st) of Mercur ore was obtained from the heap with no cement and .377 kg of NaCN/mt (.832 lb/st) was obtained from the heap with cement.

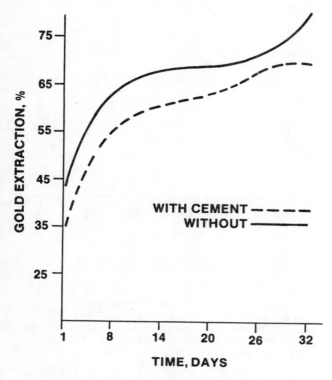

GRAPH 2. SUB-ORE AGGLOMERATION

PILOT HEAP I

ORE PREPARATION: A low grade oxide ore was crushed to -2.540 cm (-1") and agglomerated with water. During crushing, a grab sample was taken off the crushing belt every 18.14 mt (20 st) of crushed ore. A composite was made, and the sample was assayed. A 15.24 cm (6") layer of compacted sand was laid onto the PVC liner where the crushed ore was put on top using a 1:1 slope. (See Figure 3)

The ore was leached by using the preceding procedure for heap leaching.

PROCEDURE: The equipment layout used is stated in the previous heap pad methods. The heap pile was sprayed with barren solution at an approximate level of .375 kg/mt (.75 lb/t) of cyanide solution. The pH level was maintained at 9.6-10.6.

RESULTS: After 37 days of leaching, a 27.7% gold recovery was achieved. (See Graph 3)

Poor recovery was thought to be a result of poor percolation.

The cyanide consumption was .912 kg/mt (2.01 lb/st) of ore.

The heap leaching operation had a water evaporation total of .147 l per day/m^2 (.42 gal per day/sq ft) of heap. Further testing on evaporation may prove the feasibility of using reclaim water with heap leaching.

The carbon had loaded 1,903.21 gm/mt (55.510 oz/t).

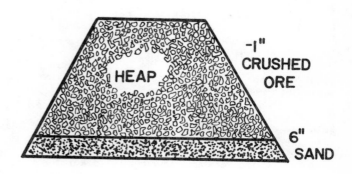

FIGURE 3. HEAP PILE CROSS SECTION

SIMULATED SAG MILL REJECTS

ORE PREPARATION: The initial sample was a composite of seven areas of the Mercur Mining District that had first been crushed and then screened to -5.08 cm (-2"), plus 2.54 cm (1").

The sample was then tumbled in batches in a cement mixer with a lime/water solution for 2 hours. The sample was then screened through a 2.540 cm (1") screen with the -2.540 cm (1") discarded. The simulated sag mill rejects were washed through the 2.540 cm (1") screen and then air dried to be ready for loading.

PROCEDURE: The equipment layout used is stated in the previous barrel test methods. A 1kg/mt (2 lb/st) of cyanide solution was sprinkled over the ore for 32 days. The cyanide solution was sprinkled at a rate of .019 l/min

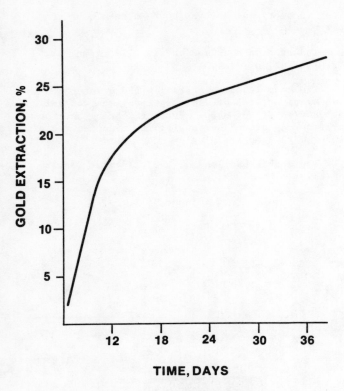

GRAPH 3.   SUB-ORE HEAP

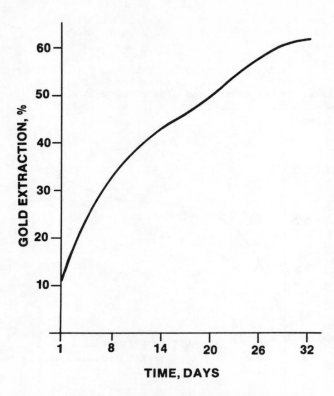

GRAPH 4.   SIMULATED SAG MILL REJECTS

(.005 gpm) per .093 sq in (sq ft). The pH level was maintained at 10.3–10.6

RESULTS: A total of 61.46% of the contained gold was extracted in 32 days of leaching. (See Graph 4)

Total cyanide consumption was 1.175 kg/mt (2.59 lb/st) for this test.

SAG REJECTS/HEAP VS. VAT

ORE PREPARATION: The sample was taken from the Mercur sag mill reject pile. There was a total of four different tests run on this sample. The samples were first split into two different piles. One pile was crushed to –2.54 cm (–1"). This crushed pile was then split again where it was weighed and put into two 378.53 1 (100-gal) leach tanks. The second pile of still whole rejects was split and then weighed while being put into the leach tanks.

PROCEDURE: One barrel with the crushed rejects and one barrel with the whole rejects were leached as stated in the preceding heap leach procedure for barrel testing. A 1kg/mt (2 lb/st) of cyanide solution was sprinkled over the ore for 10 days.

The remaining two barrels were vat leached. Using the same equipment as in the heap barrel test, each tank of rejects was completely sub-merged in 1kg/mt (2 lb/st) of cyanide solution. Every 48 hours the tank was drained into a

113.56 1 (30-gal) tank where the volume was measured and fresh cyanide solution was added for another 48 hours. This was repeated for 10 days. Each sample of solution was tested for Au and NaCN content along with the pH level.

RESULTS: After 10 days of leaching, the vat test with the whole rejects showed the best extraction and the least amount of cyanide consumption (See Graph 5)

Table No. 1

% EXTRACTED AND NaCN CONSUMPTION

Test	% Extracted	NaCN Consumption kg/mt – (lb/st)	
Crushed – Heap	17.8	.37	.74
Crushed – Vat	22.4	.39	.78
Whole – Heap	16.8	.42	.83
Whole – Vat	50.4	.36	.72

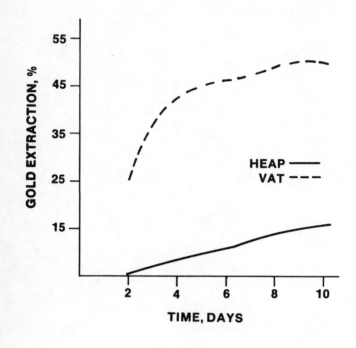

GRAPH 5.   WHOLE REJECTS

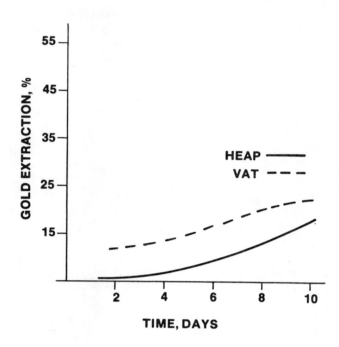

GRAPH 6.   CRUSHED REJECTS

TAILINGS

To date no testing work has been done on the old mill tailings.

SCREENING THE ORE

Presently Mercur is testing low grade ore 1.72 g/mt (.05 g/t) in a screening program to upgrade the mill feed. The mined ore is screened through a 7.620 cm (3") grizzly. The undersized is trucked to the mill. The oversized is being evaluated as potential heap leaching material.

Chapter 7

CONSTRUCTION AND INVESTIGATION OF A CLAY HEAP LEACH PAD

Dirk van Zyl
Dept. of Civil Engineering & Engineering Mechanics
The University of Arizona
Tucson, Arizona 85721

ABSTRACT

The paper describes the construction of a clay pad in Southern California. The pad consisted of a mixture of in situ soil and imported clay products. The paper summarizes design considerations. Laboratory permeability tests performed on samples removed from the pad formed part of the quality control requirement of the State of California Water Quality Control Board. The paper presents statistical analysis of the data (about 70 permeability tests in total) and their significance in controlling seepage losses. The results obtained from an investigation of the first pad-area after completion of the leach cycle are presented and discussed. Results from visual observations and laboratory tests are presented.

INTRODUCTION

Natural materials can be used successfully in the construction of heap leach pads. The use of these materials usually result in the least expensive approach for such facilities. Sufficient geotechnical experience has been gained in the design and construction of clay heap leach pads so that they can be used with confidence. A number of operators presently use clay pads in their heap leach facilities; these include Alligator Ridge, Ely, Nevada (gold), and Union Carbide, Gas Hills, Wyoming (uranium).

This paper describes the construction and field investigation of a clay pad for the heap leaching of agglomerated precious tailings. The project is located in the Mojave Desert, Southern California. The design had to satisfy operational requirements as well as regulatory requirements. The California Water Quality Control Board (WQCB) was one of the agencies which had to issue a permit for the project. Their biggest concern was the discharge or escape of cyanide into the environment. Rather stringent requirements were therefore placed on the pad design criteria, especially in terms of permeability.

Laboratory tests were performed on mixtures of insitu and imported materials and the final pad mixture was selected on the basis of these tests. The results of these tests and the construction of the pad is described. Construction quality control consisted of moisture content and density measurements. Samples were also removed for laboratory permeability tests. These tests were performed with equipment set up on site. A statistical analysis is presented of 76 permeability test results. More details on the design and the initial laboratory testing were given by van Zyl (1982).

After completing the leaching of the first heap area, an investigation was performed of the pad. The purpose of the investigation was to examine the moisture migration through the pad. Backhoe pits were excavated and samples taken for moisture content and cyanide analysis. The results of visual and analytical results are given and discussed. It is concluded that the clay pad performed very well and that a clay pad with consistently low permeability can be constructed.

REQUIREMENTS OF PAD MATERIALS

Heap leach pad materials must satisfy the following requirements:

• Permeability. The coefficient of permeability of pad material must be sufficiently low to prevent loss of leachate and therefore precious metal values. The limiting value for this economic requirement is related to the length of time that leaching will be done on a pad and the head build-up on the pad. The leaching time will determine whether the pad gets saturated during the leaching period. The coefficient of permeability of unsaturated soil is lower than that of saturated soil. Environmental concerns can result in requiring a lower permeability than would be required using the economic approach alone. However, such concerns must be related to the true potential for groundwater contamination. Very little is known about the fate of cyanide in soil (Huiatt, et al., 1983). The conservative assumption is usually made that cyanide will migrate with the same velocity as the wetting front. There is nothing to support this assumption. For the project described here, a coefficient of permeability of 5×10^{-7} cm/sec was stipulated by the WQCB as the maximum allowable value.

• Cost. There is a number of materials which can be considered for pad construction; these include: PVC, Hypalon, HDPE and other synthetic membrane type liners; rubberized asphalt which can be sprayed onto a prepared base; and soil cement or hydraulic asphalt cement. Synthetic membrane liners require a well prepared base, a cost factor which must be included in economic analyses. Insitu soil or a combination of such material and imported clay can result in a satisfactory pad. The cost of the pad material must be low enough to enhance the feasibility of the project. An economic evaluation must therefore be made, based on site specific considerations, to determine whether a clay pad is actually an economic solution.

• Pad Construction Considerations. A single use pad will require a different set of criteria than a pad which will be used for more than one leaching cycle. It is possible to re-use a clay pad; however, care must be taken not to damage the pad during the removal of heap material. A certain amount of "pumping" can occur with clay pads; i.e., moisture is "pumped" into the clay by the wheels of the construction traffic. It must also be taken into account who will do the pad construction. It can be done by the mine as a continuous process or a contractor can be hired to perform the construction. Mobilization costs in the latter alternative is an important consideration in the selection of a pad material.

• Heap Construction Considerations. The heap can be constructed by stacking the ore with front-end loaders, using belt stackers or through end dumping and dozing. The selection of a pad material is dependent on the heap construction method. For example, front-end loaders can not be used directly on synthetic materials without possibility of damaging the material. A cushion layer on top of the liner is required in this case; material for such a layer may not be available at a reasonable price.

At the project being discussed, a 43-acre pad had to be constructed over a four-year period. It was therefore decided to perform the construction as part of the mining operations. Ore stacking was to be done with front-end loaders and considerable traffic was envisioned on the pad. All these requirements led to the conclusion that a clay pad will satisfy the criteria best if suitable material could be located.

DESIGN OF MATERIAL MIXTURE FOR CLAY PAD

The soils beneath the site are generally stratified alluvial sediments deposited as a fan to a depth of about 60m. The upper portion of the subsoil contains layers of caliche, ranging in thickness from 3mm to 600mm. The soils close to the surface, and therefore that used in construction of the pad, had 20 to 30% finer than the #200 sieve and 100% finer than 35mm. This material was nonplastic and had a coefficient of permeability of 5.4×10^{-6} cm/sec when compacted to Proctor maximum density and optimum moisture content. Other materials had to be found to mix with the insitu soil to lower the permeability to the 5×10^{-7} cm/sec required by the WQCB.

A deposit of clayey silt (80% minus #200 sieve, liquid limit 50 and plasticity index 20) was found about 20km from the site. This material could be used to mix with the foundation soil. The mixture resulted in a sufficiently low laboratory permeability. The design mixture was selected through laboratory tests.

Laboratory testing for clay pad materials should consist of the following:

- Index Tests such as grain size analyses and Atterberg Limits. The results from these tests can be used to assess the characteristics of the material.

- Compaction Tests. It is recommended that the Standard Proctor Test be used. The results from this test can be used to set criteria for preparation of permeability test specimens and later to establish compaction specifications.

- Permeability Tests. Falling head or flow pump permeability tests performed on samples compacted to maximum dry density and optimum, or 1 to 2% higher than optimum, moisture content. The flow pump permeability test was described by Ketcham and Znidarčic (1981) and is based on the work of Olsen (1965, 1966). A summary of the method is given by van Zyl (1982) and is highlighted below.

It is recommended that the whole test series be repeated for all the clay mixtures used in the design process. This will help in detecting inconsistencies in the results and will allow interpolation and in some cases, extrapolation of trends. It is especially important that the permeability tests be performed on samples compacted to the same standards; otherwise, it is very difficult to compare the results from tests on the various clay mixtures and to relate the results to the expected field behavior.

Laboratory tests are conducted on specimens which are very carefully mixed to the required clay content. It is not easy to obtain an exact mix in the field. It is therefore important to build a "safety factor" into the design mix by adding some more clay than the exact required amount. There are also indications that there are differences between laboratory and field permeabilities (performed with insitu field tests) due to factors such as differences in compactive effort and cracking of the compacted material (Daniels, 1981). It is this author's opinion that these differences may not be as large as initially believed due to difficulties in performing insitu tests and in the interpretation of such test results.

Three levels of clay addition were investigated during this design of the pad mix: 10, 20 and 30% clay by dry weight was used. At 30% clay the liquid limit of the mixture was 26% and the plasticity index 9%. The coefficient of permeability was from 2 to 3×10^{-7} cm/sec. These values were well within the requirements and, as will be discussed later, close to the arithmetic mean permeability of the samples tested in the field.

Although there was sufficient confidence in the permeability of the insitu soil plus 30% clayey silt, stringent permit requirements and the need not to delay the project due to reconstruction of possible unacceptable pad, resulted in the consideration of another additive to lower the permeability of the pad even further. The pad was to be constructed to a thickness of 450mm in three layers of about 150mm thick each. The bottom and top lifts were designed using the mix above while 5% bentonite noodles was added to the middle lift. Addition of the bentonite resulted in laboratory permeability of 3×10^{-9} cm/sec.

Bentonite noodles (approximately 6mm in diameter and 10 to 20mm long) were used instead of the refined product because it was less expensive. An initial concern was that the noodles will not result in an even mix; however, it was found that an even product could be obtained by mixing the soil with some moisture in the afternoon and allowing "curing" overnight before final mixing.

It must be noted that, in general, the characteristics of the insitu soil and the clay type used as an admixture, determines the mix design. However, as a general rule of thumb, 5% bentonite is usually sufficient to lower the permeability of the mixture sufficiently. This value can be used in feasibility analysis for the comparison of natural liners with synthetic liners when suitable clays are not available on site.

CONSTRUCTION OF PAD

The total pad area of 43 acres is to be constructed over the four-year life of the project.

It was therefore constructed in cells, with dimensions of about 15m by 150m. The procedure described below was followed for the three lifts of each cell. It is common to construct more than one cell at a time or to have adjacent cells in various stages of completion. Sufficient continuity is obtained between the cells due to the disc used for mixing the materials.

After clearing the vegetation from the site, the top 150mm of soil is stockpiled for reclamation use. The site is next leveled by filling drainage channels. Next, 200 to 400mm of material is removed and stockpiled for future use in pad construction.

The soil surface is leveled with a blade before spreading a 50 to 75mm layer of clayey silt with a scraper. The materials are mixed at their natural moisture contents. Mixing is done with an agricultural disc. At least four passes with a vibratory roller are used for compaction after reaching the required moisture content.

After compaction of the bottom lift, its final surface is leveled with a blade and bentonite noodles are spread to a thickness of about 15mm. This is followed by the addition of 50 to 75mm clayey silt and 100 to 125mm of stockpiled site soil. The materials are mixed with the disc at natural moisture content. This is followed by the application of water through one or two passes of the water truck and one or two passes with the disc. The material is then left to allow the noodles to break down. Further mixing, moisture addition and compaction is done the next working day.

After compaction of the middle lift through four to five passes of the vibratory roller, the surface is again leveled and clayey silt and stockpiled soil is spread. Mixing and compaction are done as for the bottom and middle lifts.

It is preferential to have good bonding between the different layers of the pad to eliminate interfaces of preferential seepage. This is usually difficult to obtain with a smooth-wheeled roller unless the top of the previous layer is scarified. Sheepsfoot rollers enhance good bonding. However, the agricultural disc used for mixing the soils in this project promoted very good bonding because of the deep penetration of the discs.

Although the surfaces of the lifts dry out relatively fast due to the very dry climate, it is not of particular concern except for the top lift. It has been observed that only the very top few millimeters are affected through drying. Very little surface cracking has been observed on the top lift as it is regularly sprayed with water during the time that it is exposed.

CONSTRUCTION QUALITY CONTROL

Quality control testing is performed on each lift. A nuclear gauge is used to perform moisture content and density measurements. Such measurements are taken at ten locations on each constructed cell layer. Only one measurement is allowed to be outside the ranges specified below. Furthermore, laboratory permeability tests are performed on specimens removed from the pad. It was stipulated in the Waste Discharge Permit that the average permeability of the four sections of each cell must be lower than 5×10^{-7} cm/sec. Five specimens were removed from each cell. A typical sampling strategy is shown in Figure 1.

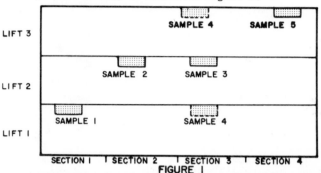

FIGURE 1
TYPICAL SAMPLING STRATEGY FOR PERMEABILITY
TESTING ON EACH 15m X 150m CELL

Compaction Control

A field compaction test, consisting of compacting test strips at different moisture contents, was performed on the mixture used for the bottom and top lifts. The maximum dry density obtained in the field was slightly higher than that from a Standard Proctor Test. Similarly, a lower optimum moisture content was obtained in the field. These results indicate a higher field compactive effort. Due to these similarities in results, a field compaction curve was not established for the middle lift material. The results from the Standard Proctor curves were used as a basis for quality control. The compaction specifications which are used consist of the following: dry density higher than 95% of maximum and moisture content in the range -2 to +2% from optimum moisture.

Most of the compaction control tests satisfied the specifications. Initially, some problems were experienced with moisture contents exceeding the upper limit, although the densities were satisfactory. These results were not of concern, as it is known that lower permeabilities are obtained if the soil materials are compacted wet of optimum.

Permeability Testing of Constructed Pad

Permeability testing of low permeability materials is very time-consuming due to long saturation times and the low percolation rates during testing. In this project permeability testing was part of the quality control requirements and results had to be obtained before construction of the next lift. It was therefore important to select a reliable testing procedure which is relatively fast to perform and gives repeatable testing results.

During the construction of a test pad, insitu permeability testing was attempted with a falling head, double-ring infiltrometer. Three major concerns with insitu permeability testing on compacted clay pad material were immediately apparent:

- severe disturbance during installation of equipment,

- relatively long testing time during which no construction equipment can be used on the lift being tested, and

- considerable concern about the boundary conditions to be used in the interpretation of test results.

The decision was therefore made to consider laboratory testing of samples removed from the constructed pad. The requirements used in selecting the testing method were those given above. It was necessary to have a method in which the sample could be saturated and the test could be performed in a relatively short time. For regular construction activities, it was required that a sample be removed in the afternoon and the results be available early the next day. In some cases, two to three days were available between the construction of the different lifts and the time requirement was then slightly relaxed.

Two methods were considered for laboratory permeability testing.

- triaxial apparatus using falling head procedure, and

- flow pump permeability testing.

Conventional laboratory permeability tests, such as the falling head test, is based on the measurement of flow rate under the application of a known gradient. The flow pump permeability test is based on the principle that water is percolated under a known flow rate through a consolidated, back-pressure saturated sample. The gradient across the sample is measured after steady-state flow is obtained and the coefficient of permeability is calculated. This method was first proposed by Olsen (1965, 1966), but has not been developed as a commercial testing technique. Research efforts at the University of Colorado over the last few years have developed flow pump permeability testing to a level where it can be applied for regular engineering testing.

The major advantages of the flow pump method are (Olsen, 1966; Znidarčić, 1982):

- pore pressure measurement is an easier and much more accurate procedure than a flow rate measurement; therefore, more accurate results are obtained and the imposed gradient can be much smaller than in either the falling head or the constant head test,

- since the flow rate is imposed by the movement of a piston in a closed cylinder (such as a syringe in a surgical flow pump) the

whole system is completely closed and there is no air-water or water-oil interface; hence, problems associated with the evaporation and/or menisci formation are eliminated, and

the apparatus could be easily set up at a remote project site which enables trained mine personnel to perform the permeability testing very rapidly.

Test specimens are removed from the constructed pad in specially machined sampling rings. These rings have a diameter of 71mm, a height of 50mm and a thin cutting edge. Sampling is done directly after the constructed lift has satisfied the moisture-density testing criteria. Specific care is taken in cutting the specimens and it is common to take one or two more specimens than required to have extras in case of specimen destruction during laboratory preparation.

Laboratory testing is performed in a ring 71mm diameter and 25mm high. The specimen is carefully trimmed in the laboratory. A thin layer of petroleum jelly is put on the testing ring before sliding the sample into it.

The apparatus designed for this project is based on a triaxial cell. After filling the cell with distilled water and de-airing the lines, a seating load is applied. Backpressure is applied and left overnight to allow saturation of the sample. The sample is then consolidated under a load of about 65 kPa (the estimated overburden pressure of the heap), before performing the permeability test. The permeability test itself usually takes 5 to 25 minutes. De-aired distilled water is used for the testing. The gradient used in the testing is typically from 1 to 10, which is of the same order of magnitude as the flow gradient through the pad under operational conditions.

The surface area of the samples tested in the laboratory is smaller than the surface area of equipment used in most insitu permeability tests. However, it is the author's opinion that the concerns raised above disturbance and interpretation of insitu permeability tests are of greater importance than the small sample area of laboratory tests. An advantage of the procedure followed here is that a large number of samples are tested and a good statistical sample is therefore obtained.

It can also be argued that only the best samples are tested in the laboratory because poor samples containing cracks and other defects will break during the trimming process and will therefore be eliminated from testing. It has been the experience during this project that very few "inferior" looking areas were observed on the pad, so that the field sampling was not biased. Furthermore, very few samples had to be rejected because of problems during sample trimming into the final rings, except due to inexperience of the personnel. The results obtained during this study can therefore be taken as representative of the pad permeabilities.

Permeability Results

A total of 76 laboratory flow pump permeability tests was performed during this project for quality control purposes. These tests consist of 41 on the top and bottom lifts (mixture of insitu soil and 30% clayey silt) and 35 on the middle lift (mixture of insitu soil, clayey silt and bentonite). Of these only seven samples from the top and bottom lifts had coefficients of permeability larger than 5×10^{-7} cm/sec. No samples from the middle lift had a coefficient of permeability higher than 5×10^{-7} cm/sec.

Histograms of the permeability data are given in Figures 2 and 3. A summary of the maximum and minimum and mean coefficients of permeability are given in Table 1.

The definitions of the means are as follows:

Arithmetic mean

$$k_a = \frac{k_1 + k_2 + \ldots + k_n}{n}$$

Geometric mean

$$k_g = \sqrt[n]{k_1 \cdot k_2 \ldots k_n}$$

For computational purposes the following form of the geometric mean can be used:

$$\log k_g = \frac{1}{n} (\log k_1 + \log k_2 + \ldots + \log k_n)$$

Harmonic mean

$$k_h = \frac{n}{\frac{1}{k_1} + \frac{1}{k_2} + \ldots + \frac{1}{k_n}}$$

where $k_1, k_2 \ldots k_n$ = coefficients of permeability from laboratory tests

n = number of samples

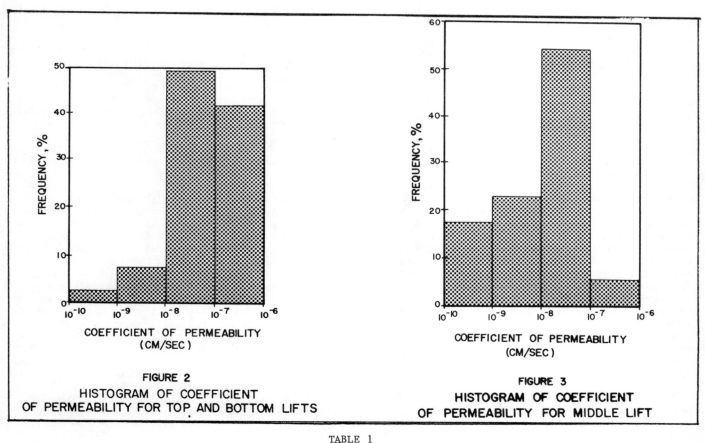

FIGURE 2
HISTOGRAM OF COEFFICIENT
OF PERMEABILITY FOR TOP AND BOTTOM LIFTS

FIGURE 3
HISTOGRAM OF COEFFICIENT
OF PERMEABILITY FOR MIDDLE LIFT

TABLE 1

Summary of Coefficients of Permeability (cm/sec)

Lift	Number of Tests	Maximum	Minimum	Mean		
				Arithmetic	Geometric	Harmonic
Top and Bottom	41	8.6×10^{-7}	8.2×10^{-10}	2.0×10^{-7}	6.9×10^{-8}	1.3×10^{-8}
Middle	35	2.7×10^{-7}	3.8×10^{-10}	3.3×10^{-8}	1.0×10^{-8}	2.2×10^{-9}

The expressions obtained for equivalent permeabilities in the horizontal and vertical directions, for a layered structure with layers of equal thickness, are identical to the expressions for the arithmetic and harmonic means, respectively. These values always represent the upper and lower bounds of the mean permeabilities while the geometric mean is between them (Bouwer, 1969).

In performing flow analysis through the pad, a choice must be made which value of mean permeability to use. For saturated flow analysis it has been found that the geometric mean is the most reliable value to use (Bouwer, 1969 and Mostyn, 1983). However, simplified partially saturated flow analyses performed during this study indicated that the harmonic mean modeled in the field observed percolation depths best. The following argument can be used to justify the use of the harmonic mean: The samples tested for permeability had equal thickness and were taken from the surface of the lift. A spatial variation of permeability is therefore obtained on that level. This spatial variation is represented by the histograms. If it is assumed that the "pad lifts" are made up by stacking these individual samples on top of each other, then the equivalent permeability for vertical flow through this stack of samples will be given by the harmonic mean permeability of the test results.

It can be concluded that the arithmetic mean permeability should not be used in seepage calculations as the results will be overly conservative.

INVESTIGATION OF PAD
AFTER LEACHING OF FIRST HEAP AREA

The waste discharge permit required an investigation of pad integrity after completing the leaching cylce on the initial heap areas. The purpose of this investigation was to determine whether any leachate penetrated the pad. Such an investigation can be made by taking samples during drilling operations or excavating the area and inspecting the subsoil in test pits. Drilling and sampling are difficult because of access to the heap and problems in retrieving undisturbed samples of the silty sand subsoil. Another concern of drilling is the possible contamination of samples during sampling. To insure reliable samples, the procedure described below was followed.

After leaching the first section of the heap for 35 days over a 60-day period, an investigation of the pad underlying the first three cells was performed. The heap materials were removed along three strips about 6m wide and 30m long by pushing the agglomerate onto the adjacent unused pad space with a bulldozer.

Ten test pits were excavated to a depth of about 2 m. The first sample hole was dug by hand. The last of the agglomerate was cleared down to the surface of the pad and an area 0.6m x 0.6m was leveled. Then, moisture and density measurements were taken with the nuclear gauge. A sample for an oven-dried moisture determination was taken using a 100mm long tube 50mm in diameter; this was driven vertically down into the pad. The next measurements and samples were taken in a similar manner after digging to the subsoil immediately below the pad. Subsequent measurements and samples were taken just above the wetting front/dry soil interface and below the moisture front.

Nine other sample holes were dug using a backhoe to make a small trench. Samples for moisture determinations and cyanide assays were collected at the pad surface, immediately below the pad, just above the moisture front/dry soil interface and below the moisture front. The location of the wetting front was easy to observe because of the clear change in soil color. In some cases only two samples were collected below the pad instead of the prescribed three, as the wetting front was so close to the bottom of the pad that three samples could not be collected. Sampling depths were measured with a tape.

Figure 4 presents a plot of moisture content versus depth for all samples taken; all the data points are shown. The solid line shows an average moisture content with depth while the dashed lines indicate a typical range of values.

The results in Figure 4 do not conclusively show that moisture penetrated the pad. The overall trend is a reduction of moisture content with depth. The "background" moisture content is reached at about 1m.

The increased moisture content below the pad can be due to three reasons:

- Wet Subsoil Due to High Rainfall Prior to Construction. Prior to and during the time when the first three cells were constructed, considerable precipitation was measured on site. The ground surface was moist before construction started.

- Moisture Which Reached the Subsoil During the Construction Process. The construction process includes discing the material in place to mix the soils and to mix in water. A 150mm layer (compacted, about 200mm loose) of materials is disced. The disc penetrates deeper than the lift thickness and therefore some moisture is worked into the foundation.

- Penetration of Leach Solution. Moisture movememt will occur under partially saturated conditions, with the moisture content increasing behind the wetting front.

It appears that the first two reasons provide the most likely explanation for the increased moisture level found below the pad. It would be expected that penetration of the pad by leach solution would be followed by an increase of moisture content in the pad. Such an increase did not occur since the moisture contents during

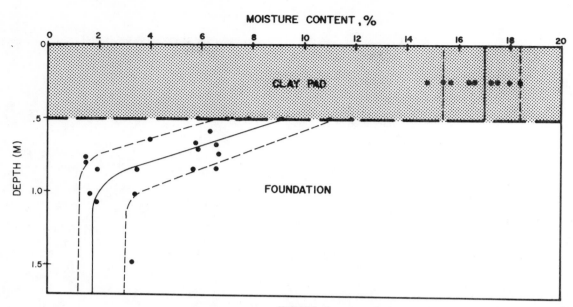

FIGURE 4

SUMMARY OF MOISTURE CONTENT DATA FROM PAD INVESTIGATION

construction and at the time of investigation were all of the same order of magnitude.

Cyanide assay results showed that no cyanide penetrated the pad during the 60-day leaching period.

CONCLUSIONS

A clay heap leach pad was constructed for the leaching of agglomerated precious metal tailings. The application of geotechnical engineering principles in the design and construction of such facilities are described. It can be concluded that reliable clay pads can be constructed for heap leach operations with the present state-of-the-art. Attention must be paid to the materials available and special testing and construction methods must be followed.

Carefully conducted laboratory permeability tests on 76 specimens removed from the constructed pad showed that the pad had a mean coefficient of permeability lower than 5×10^{-7} cm/sec. The results from an investigation of the pad after 60 says of leaching showed that no percolation took place through the pad in this period.

ACKNOWLEDGMENT

Most of the work described here was performed while the author was a full-time employee of Steffen, Robertson and Kirsten; their permission to publish this is greatly appreciated. A number of people helped in the laboratory testing, design, and construction control of the pad, noteably Messrs. Clint Strachan and Juan Rodriguez. The flow pump permeability equipment was design by Dr. Dobroslav Znidarčić, formerly of the University of Colorado, now with the University of Zagreb, Zagreb, Yugoslavia. The equipment is based upon the concept and design developed by Dr. Harold W. Olsen of the USGS. This equipment was first brought to the author's attention by Dr. Robert L. Schiffman of the University of Colorado.

REFERENCES

Bouwer, Herman, 1969, "Planning and Interpreting Soil Permeability Measurements," _Journal of the Irrigation and Drainage Division, ASCE_, September, pp. 391-402.

Daniel, D. A., 1981, "Problems in Predicting the Permeability of Compacted Clay Liners," _Proceedings, Symposium on Uranium Mill Tailings Management_, Fort Collins, Colorado, pp. 665-675.

Huiatt, Jerry L., et al., (Eds), 1983, "Proceedings of a Workshop -- Cyanide from Mineral Processing," _Proceedings_, Utah Mining and Mineral Resources Research Institute, College of Mines and Mineral Industries, Salt Lake City.

Ketcham, S. A. and Dobroslav Znidarčić, 1981, "Consolidation/Permeability Equipment, Procedures and Results for Bottom Sediment in Gas Charged Areas of Norton Sound," Report to the U. S. Geologic Survey, Branch of Engineering Geology, Denver, by Department of Civil Engineering and Architectural Engineering, University of Colorado, Boulder, Colorado, 98 pp.

Mostyn, G., 1983, "A Statistical Approach to Characterizing the Permeability of a Mass," Proceedings, 4th International Conference on Application of Statistics and Probability in Soil and Structural Engineering, Florence, Italy, Volume 2, pp. 1031-1042.

Olsen, H. W., 1966, "Darcy's Law in Saturated Kaolinite," Water Resources Research, 2, pp. 287-295.

Olsen, H. W., 1965, "Deviations from Darcy's Law in Saturated Clays," Proceedings, Soil Science Society of America, 29, pp. 135-140.

van Zyl, Dirk, 1982, "Design, Construction and Field Testing of a Heap Leach Clay Pad," Symposium on Uranium Mill Tailings, Fort Collins, Colorado, pp. 521-535.

Znidarčić, Dobroslav, 1982, "Laboratory Determination of Consolidation Properties of Cohesive Soil," Ph.D. Thesis, Department of Civil, Environmental and Architectural Engineering, University of Colorado, Boulder, Colorado, 172 pp.

Chapter 8

THE ROLE OF SOLUTION MANAGEMENT
IN HEAP AND DUMP LEACHING

W. Joseph Schlitt
Mineral & Metal Industries Department
Brown & Root, Inc.
Houston, Texas 77210

ABSTRACT

The characteristics of successful heap and dump leach operations are first reviewed in a general sense. Then attention is focussed on solution management as the key operating parameter in leaching. The first part of this study includes a detailed conceptual analysis of fluid flow. This identifies the relationships between the flow parameters and the chemical and physical properties of the rock. Then these relationships are extended to practical systems in order to establish optimum application rates and solution distribution methods for heaps and dumps.

The study shows that there is a maximum effective application rate, q_{max}, that can be used without causing solution shortcircuiting. This rate is a function of the minimum permeability in the heap or dump. The expression for q_{max} is

$$q_{max} \text{ (gal/ft}^2\text{/hr)} \approx 0.9 \text{ k (darcies)}.$$

Here k is the appropriate permeability coefficient. Using this equation, q_{max} is found to be on the order of 1 gal/ft^2/hr (4 cm/hr) for a typical heap or dump leach operation.

INTRODUCTION

A successful heap or dump leach operation requires that two general sets of criteria be satisfied. One relates to the characteristics of the ore or waste to be leached. The other involves the establishment of effective operating practices. Clearly, first consideration must be given to the characteristics of the deposit and the leach material itself. These parameters include the location of the orebody, the extent of the mineral inventory, the mineralogy and mode of occurrence of the metal values, and the chemical and physical nature of the host rock. Obviously, nature must provide a sufficient tonnage of material with adequate recoverable values per ton. Otherwise, the leach project will never reach the point where operating practices are of any consequence. These practices include heap or dump design, rock preparation and stacking, solution management, and recovery of the metal value(s).

This paper assumes an economically viable tonnage of leachable rock and focusses on solution management. This is the most universally important operating parameter in leaching. Particularly when treating mine dumps, solution management may be the only variable available for optimizing the operation. This is because the rock is treated in run-of-mine condition at locations that were selected to minimize haulage costs rather than to optimize metal recovery.

However, solution management cannot be treated as an isolated factor in leaching. This is because design considerations and rock preparation and stacking have substantial effects on solution management. For example, maximum recovery of metal values can only be achieved if the design permits good distribution and collection of leach solution. The design must also provide for movement of air into the piled rock since oxygen is needed as a reactant in solubilizing many values, including gold, silver, and sulfidic copper. Likewise, the rock must be crushed and stacked so that the minerals are accessible to solution percolating down from the surface of the heap or dump. Nevertheless, once the rock has been prepared and put in place, there

is little an operator can do except to optimize the way he handles the leach solutions. This will accomplish two things. One is to transport the lixiviant to the mineralized values throughout the piled rock. The other is to wash the solubilized values from the heap or dump to the recovery plant.

Although they clearly have a significant impact on solution management, detailed discussions of heap design and rock preparation and emplacement are outside the scope of this paper. Therefore, the interested reader is referred to the literature on these subjects. For instance, most papers on specific leach operations contain information on heap design and construction techniques. The latter can range from simple truck dumping to sophisticated agglomeration and stacking as is practiced at Ortiz (1). More generic descriptions of heap and dump design factors include those of Dahlberg (2), Cathles and co-workers, (3,4), Robinson (5), Sullivan (6) and Woodcock (7). Chamberlin (8) and Catanach (9) provide information on proper heap and dump construction techniques and McClelland and Hill (10), among others, discuss agglomeration as a method of avoiding permeability problems associated with fine material or clayey ores.

The following sections consider fluid flow in heaps and dumps from two points of view. The first deals with the conceptual aspects of the movement of solution through the piled rock. The second deals with the practical aspects of applying solutions as part of the leaching operation. Due to space constraints, no effort is made to cover the commodity- or site-specific aspects of solution management. These would include such topics as control of lixiviant chemistry and containment of leach solution within the confines of the leach system.

CONCEPTUAL ASPECTS OF SOLUTION FLOW

Static Considerations

From a theoretical point of view, solution flow in heaps and dumps involves the gravity driven, downward percolation of water in an unsaturated, semiconsolidated (porous) medium. This is a regime that remains too complex to be addressed on completely theoretical grounds. Thus, our present understanding of unsaturated flow is derived mainly from some experiments on run-of-mine rock in very large columns (11, 12), tracer studies on an actual dump (13, 14), field measurements of dump permeability (15), and various modelling efforts based on the performance of actual leaching operations (3,4,16-19).

The first step in developing some insight to solution flow through piles of rock is to categorize the space within the dump or heap. As shown in Figure 1, there are at least four distinct regions. By far the largest one is the solid rock (including isolated pores), indicated by ν_s . This represents completely stagnant space and typically involves about 60% of the total volume. Blasting and handling the rock expose pores

FIGURE 1 The Categories of Space Found Within a Heap or Dump — Solid Rock (ν_s), Open Space Within Rock Fragments (ϵ), Water-filled Void Space (ν_ℓ), Air-Filled Void Space (ν_g)

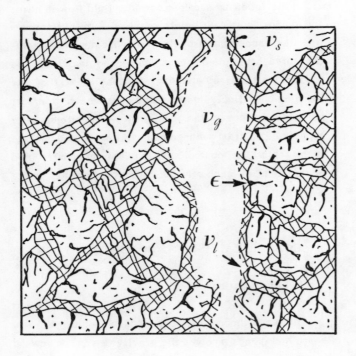

and create fractures or cracks on the faces of the rock fragments. The space associated with these openings (ϵ) is generally only 2 to 4% of the total volume. Nevertheless this space is quite important because it greatly increases the exposed surface area and makes the contained mineral values more accessible to the lixiviant. The remaining volume within the rock pile is the void space. This results from the swelling that is a consequence of fracturing and stacking the rock during mining and handling. For newly prepared heaps the void space associated with swelling normally constitutes about 40% of the volume of the rock pile. This will decrease as weathering and leaching consolidate the material. The void space will probably drop to less than 30% if a mine dump is leached over a period of years.

Obviously the void space can either be filled with solution or with air. However, because the water/rock interface has a lower surface energy than the air/rock interface, all the openings in the rock fragments will be filled with solution and the rocks themselves will be covered with water under conditions of percolation. The water-filled void space (ν_ℓ) represents the area for active water flow. On the other hand, mass transport within the ϵ -type space will occur only by diffusion. In part this is because these cracks and pores are only open at one end. Thus once the openings are filled with solution there will be no pressure gradient to cause flow into or out of the rock fragments. One other consequence of the difference in the interfacial energies is the location of the air-filled void space (ν_g). Under conditions of percolation only the larger voids and channels will contain air, as the smaller openings will be flooded.

Except under conditions of flooding, the competition between air and water for the available void space will be almost independent of the rate at which leach solution is applied. Instead, the controlling factor will be the effective particle size of the rocks in the pile. This is a consequence of the limitations imposed by capillary forces. As developed from capillary theory (20), the capillary rise or drain-down height can be calculated from Equation 1.

$$h = \frac{4\,\gamma\cos\,\theta}{g\,\rho\,d_c} \qquad (1)$$

Here h is the capillary rise, d_c is an average capillary diameter, g is the gravity constant, ρ is the liquid density, γ is the surface tension, and θ is the contact angle between the rock and the leach solution. For a typical leach solution $\gamma = 73$ dyne/cm and $\rho = 1.08$ gm/cm^3 so that h reduces to

$$h \approx 0.3/d_c \qquad (2)$$

An order of magnitude relationship can also be established between the effective particle diameter d_p and the average capillary diameter d_c. Based on 37% void space for random packing of uniform spherical particles, the relationship

$$\frac{d_c}{d_p} \approx \left(\frac{\nu_\ell}{\nu_s}\right)^{1/3} \qquad (3)$$

gives

$$d_c \approx 0.8d_p \qquad (4)$$

Appropriate substitution then gives

$$h \approx 0.35/d_p \qquad (5)$$

As shown in Table 1, this theoretical relationship is in good agreement with experimentally observed values of capillary rise which do vary with rock type (19). The same type of information is shown in Figure 2. This relates capillary rise or drain-down height to effective rock size. The same figure shows the correlation between rock size and the percentage of the total void space that remains water-filled after leaching ceases and drain down is complete. At this point capillary rise is balanced by the force of gravity and only evaporation will further reduce the water-filled void volume.

TABLE 1

CAPILLARY RISE AS A FUNCTION
OF ROCK PARTICLE SIZE

Particle Size, Mesh	Average Particle Diameter, cm	Capillary Rise, cm	
		Measured	Theoretical
10/20	0.11	3.0	3.2
20/28	0.07	4.4	5.0
28/35	0.05	8.0	7.0
35/48	0.035	14.0	10.0
48/65	0.024	19.0	14.6

FIGURE 2 Solution Retention and the Corresponding Capillary Rise as a Function of Rock Size

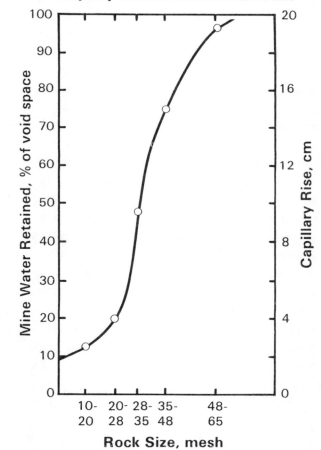

The experimental results shown in Figure 2 are significant when ingress of air is needed to aid in solubilizing the metal values. The data demonstrates that if the material is finer than about 48 mesh, it will

not drain down at all and little or no air will be able to penetrate into the pile. On the other hand, if the material is coarser than about 10 mesh, the pile will drain down almost completely.

Dynamic Considerations

Further insight into the competition between air and water for the void space can be gained by noting the changes that occur as the application rate increases.

When leaching begins at a low application rate on a thoroughly drained dump, some additional air-filled void space becomes water-filled. This occurs at air-water interfaces and flow occurs. The relative change in the water- and air-filled void space is small because the fine capillaries never drained and only a few critically sized capillaries refill with water. As the application rate increases, the only change will be to thicken the film of flowing water in the larger voids and channels where there is a solution-air interface. No substantial change in the volumes occupied by air and liquid will occur until the application rate increases to the point where the air-filled voids begin pinching off. (See Figure 3.) When such bottlenecks occur, the open voids will flood upward from the pinch points and the air-filled void spaces will begin disappearing. Experimental column data demonstrating this phenomenon is shown in Table 2. Note that at typical application rates (0.4 to 4.0 cm/hr or 0.1 to 1.0 gal/ft^2/hr) there is considerable air-filled void space. Thus, adequate aeration should not be a problem unless the material being leached is very fine, e.g., flotation mill tailings.

Regardless of the application rate, the velocity of solution flowing through a water-filled void is controlled by the pressure gradient associated with the hydrostatic head and the permeability at that location. This relationship is expressed by Darcy's law as given by equation 6 (21),

$$V_{\ell}^{\circ} = \frac{k}{\mu}\,(dp/dx) \qquad (6)$$

where V_{ℓ}° is the superficial velocity of the leach solution, k is the permeability, μ is the fluid viscosity

FIGURE 3 Schematic Representation of Void Space Flooding

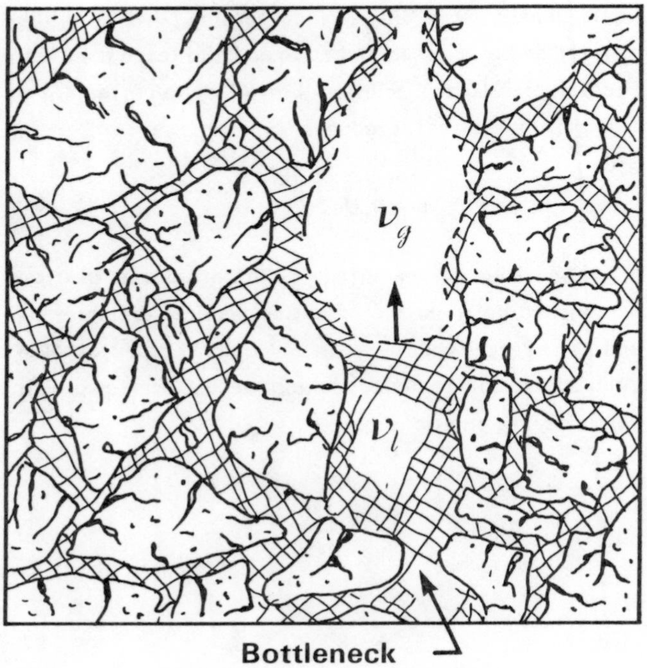

TABLE 2
EFFECT OF SOLUTION APPLICATION RATE ON THE WATER-FILLED VOID SPACE

Application Rate cm/hr	gal/ft^2/hr	Water-Filled Void Space, %*	Comments
0	0	8.0	Drained
0.12	0.03	9.6	Capillaries filled
0.60	0.15	9.7	Typical range of application rates
2.4	0.60	10.1	
12.0	3.0	10.3	
305.0	75.0	10.5	
407.0	110.0	27.6	Flooded

*Expressed as a percent of the total space within the rock pile.

and dp/dx is the pressure gradient or hydrostatic head of the leach solution. Substituting appropriate values into equation 6 gives

$$V_{\ell}^{\circ} \text{ (cm/hr)} = 3.75k \text{ (darcy)} \qquad (7)$$

Note that V_{ℓ}° is calculated as if the flow occurs over the entire cross sectional area under leach and not just in the water-filled voids.

Equation 7 also defines an equivalent maximum application rate, q_{max}, which can be used without experiencing shortcircuiting through the larger voids and channels that are partially air-filled. Using operator oriented units, this expression is

$$q_{max} \text{ (gal./ft}^2\text{/hr)} \approx 0.9k \text{ (darcy)} \qquad (8)$$

A plot of this relationship is shown in Figure 4 for the case where $\nu_{\ell} = 20\%$.

Although heaps and dumps typically contain a broad rock size distribution, the permeability and thus q_{max} will be dominated by the smaller particles that fill the interstices between the larger rocks. While intended for uniformly sized particles, the Blake-Kozeny equation* (22) can be used to establish an order of magnitude relationship between the effective particle size d_p and the permeability for a given fractional; water-filled void space. This expression is

$$k = \frac{6.7 \times 10^5 \; d_p^2 \; \nu_{\ell}^3}{(1 - \nu_{\ell})^2} \qquad (9)$$

Equations 8 and 9 can then be combined to relate the effective particle size to the maximum application rate. This correlation is also shown in Figure 4.

----

* The Blake-Kozeny relationship is only valid for laminar flow. A calculation of the Reynolds number shows that this condition holds for heap and dump leaching, with the possible exception of very high flow rates in the large channels that are partially air filled.

Since capillarity confines the leach solution to the smaller voids, flow is limited almost entirely to these capillaries when the application rate is less than q_{max}. Once the water application rate exceeds this value, the excess floods laterally and substantial flow occurs in the films along the walls of the larger air-filled voids. Further increases in the application rate simply shunt an increasing volume of water to the large channels. This leads to significant shortcircuiting of the leach solution.

Clearly the average permeability of the heap or dump matrix will limit the effective velocity or application rate that can be used to flush the solubilized values to the recovery plant. When the rate of metal extraction is controlled by washing the soluble values from the water-filled void space, use of application rates in excess of q_{max} are detrimental. Such high flows mean that higher than necessary pumping costs are incurred. The recovery plant must also handle the excessive solution flow. In addition to higher operating costs, this means that capital costs must be increased to provide the oversized facilities.

The actual flow rates involved are high even when there is no shortcircuiting. For a matrix permeability of 5 darcies (equivalent to a particle size of 35 mesh), V_{ℓ}° will be 4.5 m/day. However, the actual water velocity will be five times as high, or about 22.5 m/day assuming that the water-filled voids occupy 20% of total volume of the heap or dump. When excessive application rates shunt water to channels where k = 100 darcies, the velocity will reach 450 m/day. This explains why some outflow from the piles is often noted within a few hours after leaching commences on a previously drained area.

Even at a low application rate the high flow rate within the interior of the rock pile does more than efficiently wash dissolved values out of the heap or dump. The flow will also rapidly distribute the lixiviant throughout the liquid-filled void space. However, this will not carry the lixiviant to the undissolved mineral

FIGURE 4   Maximum Effective Application Rate (q_{max}) as a Function of the Permeability of the
Water-Filled Void Space and Corresponding Rock Size

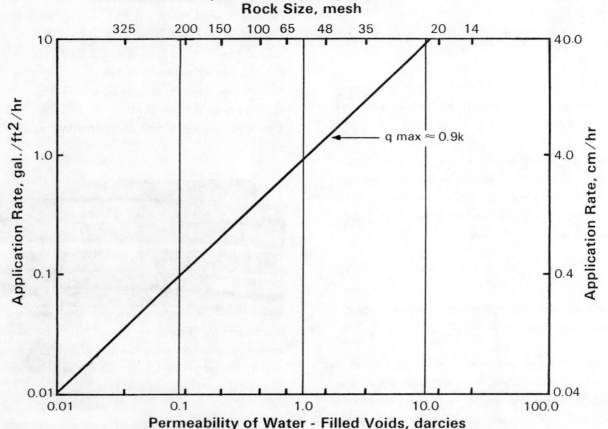

values unless these are exposed on the outer surfaces of the rock particles. As discussed above, when the values are contained within the rocks, the required lixiviant transport can only occur by diffusion. This will be orders of magnitude slower than solution flow.

As shown in Equation 10, the penetration distance, X_L, of the lixiviant will depend on the rate lixiviant consumption as well as on the diffusion rate.

$$X_L = \sqrt{D_L/K_L} \qquad (10)$$

Here D_L is the effective diffusivity of the lixiviant ion in the leach solution and K_L is the rate constant for consumption of the lixiviant when solubilizing the values. A typical room temperature value of D_L is 1.2×10^{-5} cm^2/sec and K_L will be in the order of 10^{-7}/sec. Thus effective diffusional penetration will be about 10 cm before the lixiviant is consumed.

PRACTICAL ASPECTS OF SOLUTION FLOW

Selection of the Optimum Application Rate

From the standpoint of the leach operator, the main point of the foregoing discussion is that the maximum effective application rate will be limited by the zone of minimum permeability in the system under leach. This may be the bulk permeability of the rock pile. However, care should be taken so that the solution application rate does not exceed the surface acceptance rate of the heap or dump. This value is equivalent to the maximum effective application rate and is also calculated using Equation 8. However, the appropriate k-value is that for the surface, rather than the bulk permeability. This is an important consideration because there are several factors which can combine to make the surface permeability lower than the bulk value. These factors include the following:

1. Accelerated decrepitation or weathering of the surface layer.

2. Breakup and compaction of the surface rock due to equipment movement, particularly haulage truck traffic.

3. Segregation of fine material at or near the top of the heap where dumping occurs.

4. Formation or accumulation of chemical precipitates such as gypsum or hydrated iron oxides.

Where surface permeability is lower than the bulk value, the application rate should be reduced to avoid ponding. Such surface flooding will prevent air circulation into or through the rock. Ponding will also provide ideal conditions for continued chemical precipitation that seals the surface of the rock pile.

To select the maximum effective application rate, the leach operator will need some knowledge of the range permeabilities found in his system. This information is probably best obtained by using one of the standard water permeability tests. Unfortunately, there is little published data on heap and dump permeability to serve as a guide. Limited field measurements on copper leach dumps show a distinctly bimodal distribution of values (15). The matrix has a low permeability (k = 0.3 to 3.0 darcies) but this region is intersected at intervals by major channels (k = 100 darcies). In correspondence with the matrix values, the maximum application rate should be 1.2 to 12.0 cm/hr (0.3 to 3.0 gal/ft^2/hr). Because of possible surface effects or low permeability zones, prudent leach practice suggests a range of application rates between 2.0 and 4.0 cm/hr (0.5 and 1.0 gal/ft^2/hr). Higher flows simply cause increasing amounts of water to shortcircuit through the rock without recovering additional values.

The problem of shortcircuiting may be fairly common since trickle systems using drilled or perforated pipe give application rates of 8.0 cm/hr (2.0 gal/ft^2/hr) and pond leaching may involve rates as high as 20 cm/hr (5.0 gal/ft^2/hr) (23). Further evidence of shortcircuiting is described by Murr, etal (12). These investigators observed that the copper content of solutions leaving a dump increased once application on the surface ceased. The likely explanation is that water shortcircuiting through large channels dilutes the average copper values. However, the passage of this front is so rapid that the excess flow drops off almost as soon as leaching stops. On the other hand, the capillaries will continue to drain for some time since the flow rate through these voids is slower than that in the large channels. The finest capillaries will have the greatest copper concentration and will also drain the slowest. Thus, an increase in the copper concentration would be expected as drain down progresses.

The importance of controlling the application rates is further demonstrated in data published by Kennecott for copper dump leaching (23). These results compare sprinkler leaching at 2.0 cm/hr (0.5 gal/ft^2/hr) with trickle leaching at 8.0 cm/hr (2.0 gal/ft^2/hr). Sprinkler leaching produced 11% more copper and a 15% higher copper content in the pregnant solution. Overall, 13% less water was pumped per pound of copper produced when using the lower application rate. This provided a significant reduction in power costs per unit of copper produced.

There are severals ways of obtaining the desired application rates. The popular rotating, impulse-type leach sprinklers used by Kennecott and others were originally developed for agriculture. However, when constructed of plastic and stainless steel, these units make excellent tools for "farming" heaps and dumps as well. Particularly in the larger bore sizes, these units operate without plugging over a wide range of line pressures. Figures 5-8 show typical sprinkler operating characteristics for actual leach solution as a function of line pressure. The excellent uniformity of the application rate at various distances from the sprinkler unit is highly desirable. In addition to these sprinklers, drip irrigation systems (24), and the so-called Bagdad wigglers (25) also provide effective low application rate leach systems.

As pointed out above, excessive application rates are detrimental to heap and dump leaching operations.

FIGURE 5   Sprinkler Throughput as a Function of Line Pressure for Three Sprinkler Models
Type 1, Double Bore (Spreader Driven), 5/8 in. x 1/4 in. Nozzles
Type 2, Single Bore, 9/16 in. Nozzle
Type 3, Single Bore, 5/8 in. Nozzle

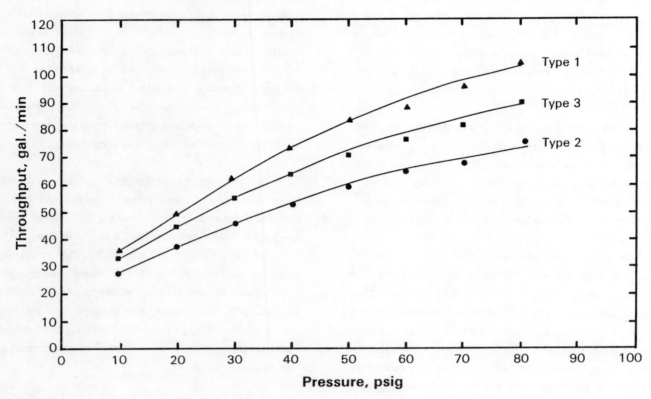

On the other hand, rates well below the value of q_{max} may not be desirable either. There seems to be little published on this problem, probably because most operators would tend to use too much water, rather than too little. However, the author's own experience suggests that the rate of extraction and perhaps even the ultimate degree of extraction are reduced at very low application rates. There are at least two reasons to account for this.

First, as the application rate decreases the hydrostatic head drops. This reduces the driving force for capillary flow. As a result, the flow through the smaller diameter capillaries will slow down or actually stop. This reduces the rate at which the values are washed out of the heap or dump.

Second, at very low flows, the water will remain in contact with both the host rock and air within the pile of rock for an extended period. Continued dissolution of various minerals (gangue as well as values) can then cause the solution to become saturated with respect to different soluble salts. This can lead to chemical precipitation within the water-filled void space or even in the openings in the rock fragments. These precipitates will tend to coat the rock or block openings so that lixiviant transport to the mineral values is reduced. Two additional factors can compound this problem. One is air oxidation of the solution and the other is evaporation at the solution-air interface. Oxidation can cause conversion of a soluble species to an insoluble one, e.g., ferrous iron oxidizing to the ferric state with precipitation of a hydrated oxide. Similarly, evaporation can cause supersaturation and precipitation of various salts. In either case the solids can plug the system and make leaching less effective.

FIGURE 6   Maximum Sprinkler Throw Radius as a Function of Line Pressure for Three
Sprinkler Models — Same types as Figure 5

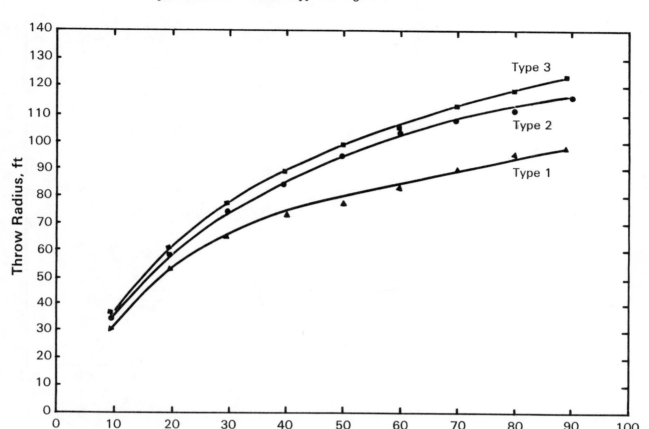

Leach/Rest Cycles

Finally, the subject of leach/rest cycles deserves some attention as a factor in solution management. As indicated earlier, once a volume of rock has been thoroughly wetted with solution, the lixiviant will be distributed throughout the rock mass. From that point on, dissolution of the values will continue without further leach solution application unless the lixiviant is consumed completely. Thus, rest cycles should not affect overall extraction of the metal values.

However, rest cycles can extend the economic life of older heaps and dumps and this permits maximum recovery of values from the material that was mined. Use of rest cycles will also permit an operator to reduce costs by maintaining a limited flow of high grade pregnant liquor to his plant. In both cases, the key factor is switching the application of water from one leach area to another. While standing fallow, chemical and diffusional processes dissolve the values and cause their concentration to build up in the water-filled void space. Then a relatively short period of active solution application will wash the solubilized values from the heap or dump. On older material a longer rest cycle may be required to build up an economic concentration prior to washing. In a similar vein, recycling barren solution to the oldest material first, then advancing the outflow to fresher material will reduce the volume and increase the grade of the pregnant solution being treated in the plant. For these reasons, leach/rest cycles should not be overlooked as a way of optimizing a leach operation.

FIGURE 7 Average Sprinkler Application Rate as a Function of Line Pressure for Three Sprinkler Models — Same types as Figure 5

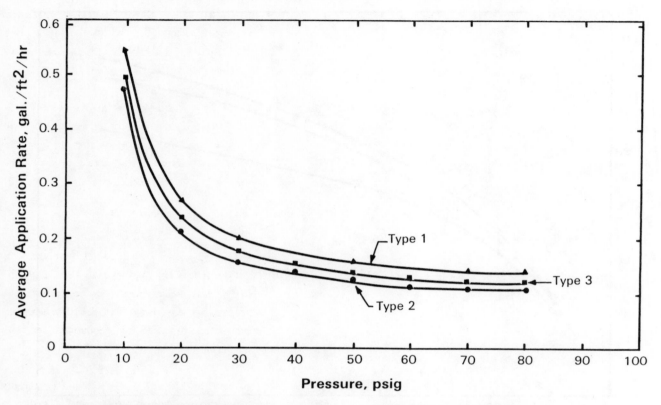

FIGURE 8 Local Sprinkler Application Rate as a Function of Distance from the Sprinkler — Type 2 (See Figure 5.)

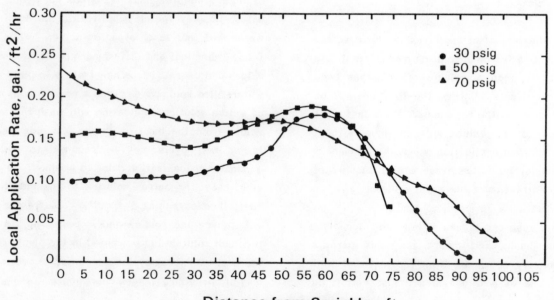

Even with a relatively short leach cycle, washing of soluble values from a heap or dump is not perceived to be a problem. This probably reflects the common practice of leaching until the concentration of the value in the pregnant solution drops to the break even point. Testwork was conducted by the author to determine the soluble copper content of drill cuttings from several leach dumps. The results showed that the water soluble copper content could be accounted for by assuming that the drained dumps contained 8% moisture at the same average copper content as that in the last outflow of pregnant solution from the dump.

SUMMARY AND CONCLUSIONS

The conceptual and practical aspects of solution management in heap and dump leaching operations have been reviewed. Principal conclusions from this analysis of fluid flow are summarized below.

1. Except under conditions of flooding, the competition between air and water for the available void space in the material under leach will be determined by the effective rock size and not by the solution application rate.

   a. Based on capillary theory, the material in the heap or dump must have an effective particle size coarser than about 48 mesh in order to have some air-filled void space and to allow for ingress of air into the rock pile.

   b. If the material is finer than about 48 mesh, capillary forces will prevent drain down so that the entire pile remains flooded unless water is removed by evaporation. Under such conditions the air needed to help dissolve the metal values will not reach the minerals.

2. The velocity of solution flowing in the water-filled void space will vary from several meters per day to several hundred. The velocity will depend on the hydrostatic head and permeability at that location, but will be independent of the solution application rate at the surface.

3. There is a maximum effective application rate, q_{max}, that can be used without causing solution short circuiting through the voids and channels that are partially air-filled. The expression is

$$q_{max} \approx 0.9k$$

   where q_{max} is given in gal./ft^2/hr and k is the permeability in darcies. Use of higher rates will raise costs for pumping and processing the water without providing an offsetting increase in production of the metal values.

   a. The value of q_{max} will be limited by the zone of minimum permeability in the system. This may be located at the surface of the heap or dump, rather than within the rock pile.

   b. For typical permeabilities of 0.3 to 3.0 darcies, prudent leach practice suggests that q_{max} should be on the order of 1.0 gal./ft^2/hr (4cm/hr).

4. The use of application rates substantially below q_{max} may be detrimental to the extraction or recovery of metal values. Contributing factors could include less effective washing of the water-filled void space and blockage or plugging of the system by precipitated salts.

5. The effective penetration of the lixiviant into the open pores and cracks in the rock

fragments will be a function of the rate of lixiviant consumption as well as its diffusion coefficient in solution. This penetration will be on the order of 10 cm for material when it is first placed under leach.

6. Theoretically, leach/rest cycles will not increase the dissolution rate of the minerals. However, such cycles can be used to achieve maximum extraction from the mined materials while maintaining an economic concentration of values in the pregnant solution.

REFERENCES

1. Hickson, R. J., "Heap Leaching Practices at Ortiz Mine, Santa Fe County, New Mexico," Interfacing Technologies in Solution Mining, W. J. Schlitt, Ed., SME-AIME, New York, 1982, pp. 209-222.

2. Dahlberg, H. R., "Heap Leaching as a Unit Process," SME-AIME Preprint #79-308, 1979.

3. Cathles, L. M. and Apps, J. A., "A Model of the Dump Leaching Process that Incorporates Oxygen Balance, Heat Balance, and Air Convection," Met. Trans. B, Vol. 6B, 1975, pp.617-624.

4. Cathles, L. M. and Schlitt, W. J., "A Model of the Dump Leaching Process that Incorporates Oxygen Balance, Heat Balance and Two Dimensional Air Convection," Leaching and Recovering Copper from As-Mined Materials, W. J. Schlitt, Ed., SME-AIME, New York, 1980, pp. 9-27.

5. Robinson, W. J., "Finger Dump Preliminaries Promise Improved Copper Leaching at Butte," Ming. Eng., Vol. 24, 1972, pp. 47-49.

6. Sullivan, J. D., "Chemical and Physical Features of Copper Leaching," Trans. AIME, Vol. 106, 1933, pp. 515-546.

7. Woodcock, J. T., "Copper Waste Dump Leaching," Proc. Australasian Inst. Ming & Metall., No. 224, 1967, pp. 47-66.

8. Chamberlin, P. D., "Heap Leaching and Pilot Testing of Gold and Silver Ores," Ming. Cong. J., Vol. 67, 1981, pp. 47-52.

9. Catanach, C. B., "Development and In Place Leaching of Mountain City Chalcocite Ore Body," Extractive Metallurgy of Copper, Yannopoulos, J. C. and Agarwal, J. C., Eds., TMS-AIME, New York, 1976, pp. 849-872.

10. McClelland, G. E. and Hill, S.D., "Heap Leaching Gold-Silver Ores with Poor Percolation Characteristics," Gold and Silver - Leaching, Recovery and Economics, Schlitt, W. J., Larson, W. C. and Hiskey, J. B., Eds., SME-AIME, New York, 1981, pp. 43-50.

11. Murr, L. E., "Observations of Solution Transport, Permeability, and Leaching Reactions in Large, Controlled, Copper-Bearing Waste Bodies," Hydromet., Vol. 5, 1979, pp. 67-93.

12. Murr, L. E., Schlitt, W. J. and Cathles, L. M., "Experimental Observations of Solution Flow in the Leaching of Copper-Bearing Waste," in Interfacing Technologies, op. cit., pp. 271-290.

13. Howard, E. V., "Chino Uses Radiation Logging for Studying Dump Leaching Processes," Ming. Eng., Vol. 20, 1968, pp. 70-74.

14. Armstrong, F. E., Evans, G. C., and Fletcher, G. E., "Tritiated Water as a Tracer in the Dump Leaching of Copper," U. S. Bureau of Mines RI 7510, 1971.

15. Whiting, D. L., "Hydrology of Dump Leaching and In-Situ Solution Mining," SME-AIME Preprint #77-AS-336, 1977.

16. Harris, J. A., "Development of a Theoretical Approach to the Heap Leaching of Copper Sulfides," Proc. Australasian Inst. Ming. & Metall., No. 230, 1969, pp. 91-92.

17. Roman, R. J., "Solution Channeling in Leach Dumps," Trans. AIME, Vol. 262, 1977, pp. 73-74.

18. Jacobsen, R. H., et al., "Optimization of Dump and Heap Leaching — Theoretical and Practical Studies" Print No. T IV a 3, Joint Meeting, MMIJ-AIME, Tokyo, May 1972.

19. Sullivan, J. D., Keck, W. E., and Oldright, G. L., "Factors Governing the Entry of Solutions into Ores During Leaching," U.S. Bureau of Mines Tech. Paper No. 441, 1929.

20. Sheehan, W. F., Physical Chemistry, Allyn & Bacon, Inc., Boston, 1961, pp. 98-99.

21. Bird, R. B., Stewart, W. E., and Lightfoot, E. N., Transport Phenomena, J. Wiley & Sons, New York, 1960, pp. 149-150.

22. Ibid., pp. 196-200.

23. Jackson, J. S. and Ream, B. P., "Solution Management in Dump Leaching," in Leaching and Recovering Copper, op. cit., pp. 79-94.

24. Rudy, W., "Heap Leaching at Cyprus Johnson," Arizona Conf. of AIME, May 1978.

25. Chamberlain, P. G. and Pojar, M. E., "The Status of Gold and Silver Leaching Operations in the United States," in Gold and Silver, op. cit., pp. 1-16.

Chapter 9

Engineering Design for the Recovery of Precious Metals from Heap Leach Solutions

Roger M. Nendick
Kilborn Engineering (B.C.) Ltd.
1380 Burrard Street
Vancouver, B.C., Canada V6Z 2B7

Abstract

The recovery of precious metals from heap leach solutions can be accomplished by two processes:

1. The Carbon Adsorption Process

2. The Merrill-Crowe Zinc Precipitation Process

A brief review of the relative process economics is made. Each process presents certain design considerations that must be addressed during the evaluation and engineering design for the project. Discussion is presented on the design criteria for each process.

INTRODUCTION

Heap leaching of precious metal ores was first practiced on a commercial scale at Cortez Gold Mines, Nevada in 1971, following two years of development work by that company and by the U.S. Bureau of Mines. The process proved to be a technically successful and profitable method for treating low grade ores. The process was rapidly investigated and adopted by other mining companies with a success rate that generally reflected the amount of planning each company put into each project.

The successful design of a heap leach recovery plant requires a careful evaluation of many engineering parameters. Almost by definition, a heap leach operation has to have a low capital cost per ton of capacity and there is little room for expensive mistakes.

The stages of development for a heap leap project are the same as for other mining projects.

Exploration

Preliminary Feasibility Study and Metallurgical Testing

Detailed Engineering and Construction

Commissioning and Operation

Exploration

The location of the deposit is under the control of a higher authority than the Project Manager. It must be accepted that the Project must be constructed at the site of the orebody as heap leach ores will not tolerate the cost of long distance trucking.

Preliminary Feasibility and Metallurgical Testing

This comprises order of magnitude cost estimates carried out in conjunction with metallurgical testing. It is important to evaluate all applicable processes for the ore i.e. Heap Leaching, Cyanide Milling and Flotation etc., prior to deciding on the preferred process.

Feasibility Study

The feasibility study will probably be used to raise outside finance or support an internal company A.F.E. As such it is imperative that a realistic appraisal of the capital and operating costs is made. If a project appears feasible at a capital cost of, say, $10,000,000 then financing of $10,000,000 should be arranged and not $8,000,000 that might be adequate only with a lot of luck.

Detailed Engineering and Construction

This step will ultimately decide the success or failure of the operation. Close attention must be paid to scheduling so that the Project can be completed and start paying back on time.

Operation

It is important to have key personnel with experience of the heap leach process, thereby removing several steps from the learning curve associated with an operation. It is recommended that one Senior Process Manager work with the Engineer during the detailed engineering so that a mutually acceptable installation is constructed. It is not recommended to have the Process Manager hired to run an operation whose design he is not fully in agreement with.

PROCESS ECONOMICS

Following the development of the heap leach process, some ill-judged decisions were made to start heap leach operations without careful study of the technical or financial considerations. The deserts of the southwest are littered with small scale heap leach operations that did not achieve the metallurgical or financial recoveries expected.

As a general statement, heap leaching is applied to low grade ores with a gold equivalent value of less than 0.1 oz per ton. How much less than 0.1 oz per ton is generally a function of the scale of operation.

Heap Leaching vs Milling

The economics of the heap leach operation arises from, the low cost of comminution as compared to a conventional mill, generally two-stage crushing is adequate for heap leaching, and from the elimination of liquid solid separation or carbon-in-pulp stages.

Building costs are generally lower because of the simpler plant design involved.

An in-house study has been carried out to assess the relative economics of heap leaching and C.I.P. milling operations for various ore grades and tonnages. Clearly, many assumptions had to be made for such a study, namely:

1) Metallurgical recoveries would be 20 percent higher by C.I.P. milling.
2) Gold Price U.S. $450 per oz.
3) Mine Life 10 years.
4) Heap Leach 8 month operation per year, C.I.P. 12 month operation.

The estimate quality was by factored cost from equipment purchase cost, and as such should only be regarded as plus minus 30 percent accuracy.

The study concluded that for operations above 5000 tpd a C.I.P. plant generally produced a better rate of return.

Figure (1) shows the relationship between ore grade and size of operation required to justify the construction of a C.I.P. mill.

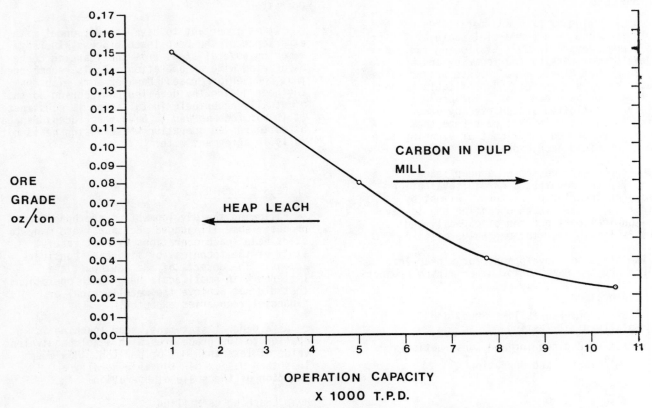

Figure 1. Comparison between Heap Leaching and Carbon-in-Pulp Mill
for Processing Gold Ores (capacity vs ore grade)

Carbon Adsorption vs Merrill Crowe Recovery

Assuming that the economic evaluation has dictated a heap leach operation, then the choice of gold recovery process for the leach solution must be made.

A further study was conducted on hypothetical cases to assess the variables influencing this choice.

Factors that affect the choice are:

1) Grade of Ore (solution).
2) Tonnage of Solution.
3) Clarity of Pregnant Solution.
4) Degree of Solution Fouling.

Some of these factors cannot be assessed economically but, in a comparison of ore grade and tonnage, the evaluation concluded that the high grade low tonnage operations clearly favoured a Merrill-Crowe System.

Essentially high grade ores produce a large number of ounces of precious metal. At a finite carbon loading capacity, this increases the quantity of carbon to be handled and proportionately increases the capital cost.

A graph of the findings is shown in Figure 2.

Metallurgical Testing of Heap Leach Operations

For any metallurgical operation it is essential that sufficient metallurgical testing be conducted to provide an adequate design basis for engineering work, and to provide a degree of confidence that the expected metallurgical performance is achievable. This degree of confidence required will increase with the sum of capital to be invested.

The major areas to be investigated are:

1) The Leach Extractions.
2) Percolation Rates.
3) Carbon Loading.
4) Solution Fouling.
5) Impurities (mercury).

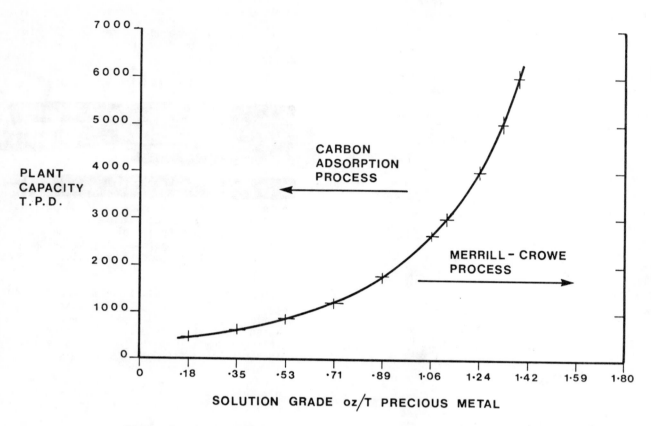

Figure 2.   Capital Cost Comparison between the Carbon Adsorption Process
and the Merrill-Crowe Process   (capacity vs solution grade)

The heap leach extraction and percolation rates are beyond the scope of this paper but it should be cautioned that care must be taken in interpretting leach results. If possible, a pilot scale heap should be tested.

PLANT DESIGN CONSIDERATIONS

Having established that heap leach operations are generally applicable to extremely low grade ores, then it is clear that the plant design must be extremely cost effective in order to make the project a viable proposition.

Some factors fortunately assist a cheap plant design:

Because most of the heavy equipment associated with a conventional mill is redundant in a heap leach operation, foundations and excavation work can be minimized.

Generally light pre-engineered structures can be used with a minimal amount of internal plat-forming. Erected costs of structures of between $10 and $20 per square foot are not uncommon.

Power requirements of 6 to 10 kWh per ton are generally adequate for heap leaching. It is therefore feasible to supply power with light diesel generating units on remote areas.

The heap leach process is very adaptable to the scale of operation requirements. It is relatively simple to start out with a minimal number of process steps and then add on other stages as the scale of operation increases.

Specific design considerations are:

CARBON ADSORPTION PROCESS

Carbon Column Design

Carbon columns are a simple efficient method of removing precious metals from a cyanide solution. Particular advantages of carbon columns are:

1)   Low cost.
2)   Ability to handle solution with small amounts of solids.
3)   Ease of operation.

For all these advantages the design of a carbon column circuit requires close consideration.

Figure 3 shows a typical carbon column design. The pregnant solution upflows via the distribution/baffle plate. The simplest design for the baffle is to use two perforated plates with the holes off-centre in relation to each other. This permits solution to flow upwards but carbon cannot fall to the lower chamber during shut downs.

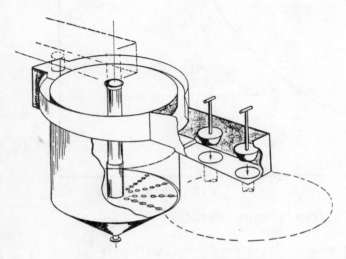

Figure 3. Typical Carbon Adsorption Cone with Bypass Arrangement (after McQuiston and Shoemaker)

The correct degree of fluidization of the carbon is essential for good operation. Under fluidization results in plugging of the columns by fine suspended solids in the solutions and over fluidization results in loss of carbon in carryover from the top of the column. Operating data shows that the optimum design flow is 30 usgpm per square foot of column area.

The requirements for easy operation are a consistant feed rate to the column and an even distribution of the flow across the column to prevent channeling. It is suggested that it is better to slightly undersize the columns and recirculate some pregnant solution to the heaps as depicted in Figure 4. This arrangement eliminates the need for costly automatic speed controls and flow regulators and insures a constant flow rate and fluidization of the bed.

In some cases it may be necessary to use a centre feed in order to get equal flow distribution across the column. It appears that columns above 8 feet in diameter need to be fed from the centre. For smaller columns it is possible to feed the solution to the side of the column below the baffle plate.

Carbon Transfer

The use of water eductors for transferring carbon is widely used in order to minimizing carbon degradation.

Important design considerations are:

The transfer solution, generally water or barren solution, should be at a consistently high pressure of approximately 60 psi. The use of a dedicated pump solely to supply eductor solution is strongly recommended.

Piping should allow for large radius elbows to minimize carbon impact and degradation. For high head transfers, as much as 15,000 gallons of water can be required to move one ton of carbon. This quantity of solution should be recognized in the impact it can have on the solution flow balance and appropriate allowances made.

Alternatives to eductors for carbon transfer include tote bins, particularly for small operations, and recessed impeller pumps. The recessed impeller pumps differ from standard centrifugal pumps in that there is no direct contact between the impeller and the slurry, therefore degradation of the carbon is minimized. The pumps are particularly useful for high head tranfers as a high density slurry can be transferred, minimizing the quantity of solution required.

Carbon Desorption (Stripping)

The choice between pressure stripping and atmospheric stripping generally is determined by the scale of operation. Large operations can generally justify pressure stripping because of the reduced time period required for stripping with this process, thereby reducing the carbon and precious metals locked up in the circuit. Smaller operations tend to favour atmospheric stripping because of the lower capital cost.

The use of the alcohol strip is an attractive compromise but the fire risks must be considered.

Refining

The oil or gas fired reverberatory furnaces have a low initial purchase price but the installed cost rises because of the increased space and ventilation requirements. Electric induction furnaces are expensive to purchase but the lower installation cost and easier operation can make them an attractive alternate.

The presence of mercury in the ore can be an influence on the refinery design. Mercury follows gold through the process and ultimately reports to the electrowinning cathodes. Apart from the necessity to install a retort ahead of refining the design should also include a small sump pump in the refinery area so that the refinery can

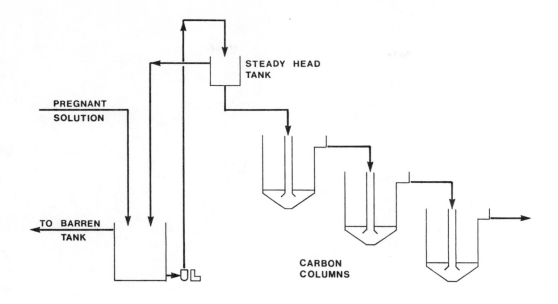

Figure 4. Carbon Adsorption Circuit with Reciruclation of Pregnant Solution

be hosed and scrubbed periodically. The provision of a parallel electrowinning circuit permits the cooling of one cell prior to removing the cathodes thereby reducing the amount of mercury vapour released when the cell is opened.

Carbon Regeneration

Intermittent thermal reactivation of the carbon is required at nearly all properties. The recent introduction of the vertical reactivation kiln can significantly reduce the capital cost of this installation both in terms of the kiln purchase price and the space required for installation. Operating data on the kiln is not readily available although several installations are about to go into the operation.

Acid treatment facilities for the removal of line scale require close attention to details. Of paramount importance is adequate ventilation to remove hydrogen cyanide fumes. If the climate permits, it is strongly recommended that the facility is located in the open, remote from the main plant area.

MERRILL-CROWE PROCESS

The necessity to clarify solutions ahead of zinc precipitation is a major disadvantage to the Merrill-Crowe Process. The use of automatic pressure filters can reduce the operating manpower required but disposal of the slurried slimes can create a problem. In net evaporation areas this can be achieved in an evaporation pond, but in areas with a net precipitation gain the use of plate and frame pressure filters may be favoured because of the dry cake discharge.

Similarly, for precipitation the plate and frame press is favoured over the more elaborate 'Stellar' type installations. For the low grade ores that are typically heap leached the high capital cost of these installations cannot be justified.

Water Balance

It is significant that the initial and subsequent development of heap leaching has taken place in Nevada. Virtually all the operations are relatively 'clean' i.e. free of base metals and sulphides. This permits solutions to be recircultated continuously without any major fouling of the leach solution. When solution needs to be disposed of it can be let to evaporation ponds.

To engineer a plant in a net precipitation area presents considerably more problems than for net evaporation areas. The net gain of solution must be treated and disposed of to a receiving waterway. The attendant permitting problems add significantly to the cost and schedule of the project.

Abandoned heaps or tailings disposal dumps must have catchment ponds to corral the cyanide bearing run-off.

Irrespective of the evaporation rate, provision must be made in the circuit design to accommodate the run-off from storms. One attractive alternate is to install the additional capacity as a second pregnant solution pond. This not only permits catchment of pond run-off but also permits routine cleaning of silt and debris by alternating ponds without interrupting production.

Chapter 10

COMPARISON OF PROCESS ALTERNATIVES FOR GOLD RECOVERY FROM CYANIDE LEACH SOLUTIONS

Michael B. Mooiman
Jan D. Miller
Dept. of Metallurgical Engineering
University of Utah
Salt Lake City, Utah 84112

J. Brent Hiskey
Kennecott Corporation
P.O. Box 11248
Salt Lake City, Utah 84147

Anton R. Hendriksz
Bateman Process Services, Inc.
777 South Wadsworth Blvd.
Lakewood, Colorado 80226

ABSTRACT

Both conventional and nonconventional process alternatives for gold recovery from cyanide heap leach solutions are discussed in terms of possible flowsheets. Conventional process alternatives include carbon adsorption and zinc dust precipitation, while nonconventional process alternatives include resin ion exchange, solvent extraction, and direct electrowinning. These strategies for gold recovery are compared on the basis of technological features and on the basis of process economics. Review of the technology status and process economics suggests that improvements for conventional process alternatives are possible and that further development of nonconventional process alternatives is warranted.

INTRODUCTION

Cyanidation of gold and silver ores by conventional mining and milling techniques has been practiced for over a century. During the past decade, heap leaching has emerged as a viable process for treating certain gold and silver ores (Chamberlain and Pojar, 1981). The rapid development of heap leaching for gold and silver ores is largely a result of lower capital and operating costs and faster start-up time than that offered by conventional mining and milling. In general, these features make heap leaching an ideal approach for exploiting either small or large low-grade disseminated deposits of gold and silver considered to be uneconomic by conventional methods. The development of heap leaching technology has evolved from the operations initiated in the western United States.

The basic components of a typical heap leaching operation are depicted in Figure 1. Run-of-mine or crushed ore (usually 1 to 5 ppm gold) is delivered to specifically prepared impervious pads. Alkaline cyanide solution is applied to the surface of the heap and allowed to percolate through the heap (typically 10-30 ft high). Pregnant leach solution which drains from the heap is collected and stored in tanks of sufficient size or in collection reservoirs. Gold and silver are recovered from the pregnant solution and the barren solution is recirculated back to the heaps after reagent make-up.

Carbon adsorption and zinc precipitation are the principal methods used to recover gold and silver from heap leach solutions; however, there are several proven alternatives already available and others emerging that show promise. Some of the alternative methods for recovering gold and silver include: resin ion exchange, direct electrowinning, solvent extraction, aluminum precipitation, and sulfide precipitation.

With every recovery option, except carbon and resin adsorption, suspended solids must be eliminated from the process stream. Typical heap leach solutions may contain anywhere from 10 to 300 ppm total suspended solids but can fluctuate widely from these values depending on such factors as weather, ore type, age of the heaps being leached, and ore agglomeration. Therefore, the flowsheet shown in Figure 1 includes a step for clarifying the pregnant liquor. The clarifier should be capable of reducing the TSS concentration in the range of 2-5 ppm.

Even though there has been considerable interest in developing alternatives to cyanidation (i.e., thiosulfate, thiourea, and brines), dilute alkaline cyanide solution remains the preferred lixiviant for leaching gold and silver ores. Table 1 reports the concentrations of selected components in some actual solutions from heap leaching operations using alkaline cyanide.

New developments in heap leaching have dealt with improving the leaching part of the operation and have not examined metal recovery from solution. For example, there have been major attempts to improve the design and construction of heaps, to stabilize slimes (agglomeration) for improved

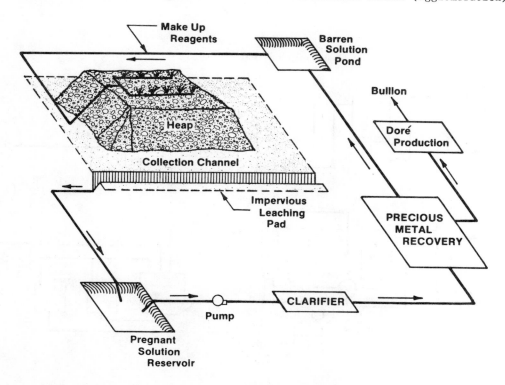

Figure 1. General layout of a heap leaching operation.

Table 1. Typical Flows and Leach Solution
Composition for Heap Leaching Operations

		Concentration							
Plant	Flowrate gpm	Au ppm	Ag ppm	Cu ppm	Hg ppm	Fe ppm	Hardness ppm	CN g/l	pH
A	500	1.0	–	<5	1-8	<1	350	–	10.5
B	1350	1-2	2.1	24.1	<1	<1	313	0.24	9.8
C	500	1.0	1.4	20.0	6.0	–	900	0.75	10.0
D*	35	1.5	0.7	4.1	75.0	0.39	164	0.14	9.3

*Test heap

solution percolation and enhanced gold and silver
recovery, and to modify solution chemistry to increase metal extraction. Recently there have been
both laboratory and pilot-scale studies directed
at improving metal recovery from cyanide solution
(i.e., resin ion exchange (Fleming, 1982), solvent
extraction (Mooiman and Miller, 1983), and direct
electrowinning (HSA Reactors Limited, 1982)).

This paper reviews the technological status of
selected recovery options and presents an economic
analysis in terms of operating and capital costs
of these processes. Promising process alternatives are examined and areas for future research
and technological development are identified.

TECHNOLOGY STATUS

Gold recovery from alkaline cyanide solution is
typically accomplished by carbon adsorption or
zinc cementation (Merrill Crowe). These and other
emerging technologies, particularly resin ion
exchange, solvent extraction, and direct electrowinning, are discussed, emphasizing the unique
features of each process alternative.

Carbon in Column (CIC)

The essence of the carbon-in-column process alternative is the adsorption of gold from alkaline
cyanide solution by activated carbon. A concep-

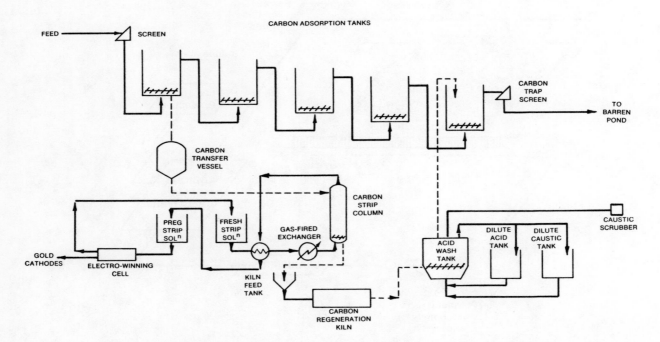

Figure 2. Flowsheet for gold recovery by the carbon-in-column process.

tual flowsheet for this process is presented in Figure 2. For typical carbon-in-column operation, the cyanide leach solution is pumped upward through columns at a flowrate of 15 to 25 gpm/ft^2, fluidizing the packed bed of activated carbon (16x30 mesh). A carbon-loading level, frequently of 200 oz/ton, is achieved while the carbon is advanced countercurrent to the solution through a staged circuit. The carbon is advanced at a rate necessary to achieve the desired level of loading. Excessive loading generally results in gold losses to the barren solution. The staged circuit could be replaced by a continuous ion exchange contactor, resulting in a substantially smaller plant and easier operation.

The loaded carbon is educted to the elution column and the gold may be stripped by different techniques as suggested in Table 2. A common procedure is to strip with 0.1% NaOH and 0.1% NaCN at 130°C and 2 bed volumes of strip solution per hour. The concentration of the pregnant strip solution is generally suitable for electrowinning of the precious metals.

Activated carbon prepared from coconut shells is preferred for gold recovery from alkaline cyanide solutions. These carbons are distinguished by high surface areas (> 1000 m^2/g), a narrow range of pore sizes (10-20 Å) and good mechanical strength. Carbon regeneration is required to remove organics and restore the intrinsic chemical activity of the carbon. After removal of carbonate deposits by an acid wash (if necessary), the carbon is activated by a thermal treatment in a kiln at 600-800°C.

Complete understanding of the gold/cyanide adsorption and desorption reactions is lacking. High surface areas and pore diffusion are important aspects of the adsorption process. A number of adsorption mechanisms have been suggested to describe the nature of the adsorbed species:

* Anion Exchange, $Au(CN)_2^-$
* Precipitation of Insoluble AuCN
* Pore Reduction to Au°
* Cluster Formation

Generally it has been found that the CN/Au ratio of the adsorbed species lies between 2/1 and 1/1 and investigators have been inclined to subscribe to the idea that adsorption involves cluster formation. This proposed mechanism together with different site functionality and pore diffusion transport provides great flexibility in accounting for the behavior of the system -- slow loading rates, some chemical specificity, and severe conditions for stripping.

Table 2. Gold Stripping from Loaded Carbon

Process	Eluant	Temperature	Time	Comments
USBM[19] Homestake	1% NaOH 0.2% NaCN	90°C	50-60 hr	Slow desorption,
AARL[3] South Africa	1% NaOH 5% NaCN presoak plus water	110°C	6 hr	Autoclave elution under pressure
Alligator[14] Ridge	1% NaOH 0.1% NaCN	120°C (25 psi)	9 hr	0.5 hr presoak
Smoky[10] Valley	1% NaOH 0.1% NaCN	88°C	52 hr	1 day presoak
Ortiz[7]	1% NaOH 0.5% Ethanol	85°C	24 hr	Safety
Battle[9] Mountain	20% Ethanol 1% NaOH 0.1% NaCN	77°C	24 hr	Safety
Anglo[11] American	90% acetone ethanol methanol	70-90°C	6 hr	Safety, Reflux solvent, Vapor losses
Murdoch[17]	20-40% organic	25°C	8 hr	Safety Organic losses New technology

Merrill-Crowe Precipitation (MC)

The Merrill-Crowe zinc-dust precipitation process is a mature and well-known technology consisting of solution clarification, deaeration,
precious metal precipitation, and precipitate filtration. A conceptual flowsheet for the Merrill-
Crowe process is presented in Figure 3. Cementation of gold onto a metallic zinc surface is represented by the following reaction:

$$2Au(CN)_2^- + Zn = 2Au + Zn(CN)_4^{2-}$$

A similar reaction can be written for silver precipitation. Historically, gold cementation with
zinc shavings was practiced in South Africa as
early as 1888 (Clennell, 1915). Zinc-dust precipitation known as the Merrill system was introduced in 1897 in the United States and is the
basis of modern practice. T. B. Crowe in 1918
patented the process for removing dissolved oxygen
from gold-bearing solution prior to addition of
the precipitating agent. This approach improved
the efficiency of gold precipitation and decreased
zinc consumption. Early cyanide practice involved
contacting zinc shavings with a solution of lead
acetate to establish a powerful galvanic couple
between the finely divided lead deposit and the
zinc surface. This procedure provides a substrate
capable of recovering gold from solutions low in
free cyanide concentration. Lead nitrate or acetate is added along with Merrillite (zinc dust) in
many modern recovery plants.

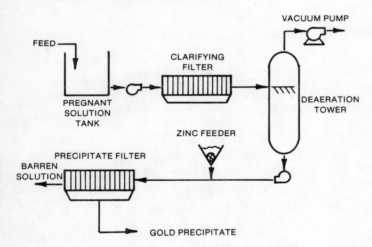

Figure 3. Flowsheet for gold recovery by the
           Merrill-Crowe process.

Clarified pregnant solution is drawn by vacuum
into the Crowe tower to lower the dissolved oxygen
concentration to less than 0.5 mg/l. Zinc dust is
added at an unspecified rate, far in excess of
stoichiometry, to the pregnant solution in such a
way as to limit the ingress of atmospheric oxygen. The slurry of precious metal precipitate and

unreacted zinc is pumped directly to a precoat
pressure filter system. Zinc dust can be added to
the precoat material (i.e., diatomaceous earth) as
a safety measure. Typical precipitate analyses
vary between 10% and 40% Au. It is clear from the
high zinc consumption that further research effort
is warranted which could result in a substantial
reduction of operating costs.

The grade of the precipitate can be increased
by either consuming excess zinc in the filter cake
by washing with pregnant solution while the zinc
feeder is off or dissolving excess zinc with sul-
furic acid after removing the precipitate from the
filter press. The precious metal filter cake is
then smelted into bars.

Silver is often recovered by zinc precipitation
instead of carbon adsorption because of the high
silver concentration and the poor silver-loading
characteristics of carbon.

Resin In Column (RIC)

Ion-exchange resins for the recovery of gold
from cyanide solution is an emerging technology
which is receiving considerable attention. The
flowsheet for the resin-in-column plant is similar
to that for a carbon-in-column (CIC) plant. See
Figure 4. The loading section is virtually identical; however, the elution (stripping) section is
different as elevated temperatures and pressures
are not required as in carbon stripping. Pressur-
ized elution vessels and heat exchangers are
therefore unnecessary. Again the continuous ion
exchange contactors can be considered for resin-
in-column as they were as in the CIC case.

Even though the exchange kinetics are faster
than the kinetics of adsorption by carbon, it does
not necessarily mean that less resin and smaller
loading columns can be used. To the contrary, as
resin beads are smaller and generally less dense
than carbon granules, slower flowrates (typically
6 gpm/ft^2 compared to 16 gpm/ft^2 for carbon) are
required to prevent the resin bed from being inad-
vertently transported to the next stage. In other
words, flowrate limitations rather than exchange
kinetics determine the reactor size. This problem
could be solved if dense and/or large resin beads
were available. Research to this end is in progress, and the results to date are very promising
(Hendriksz, 1983).

Strong or weak base resins can be used, and the
loading reactions for these resins can be des-
cribed as follows, where |— represents the poly-
meric resin matrix.

Strong Base

$$|-NR_3^+ \ X^- + Au(CN)_2^- \ \rightleftharpoons \ |-NR_3^+ \ Au(CN)_2^- + X^-$$

Weak Base

$$|-NR_2 + H^+ + X^- \rightleftharpoons \ |-NR_2H^+X^-$$

$$|-NR_2H^+X^- + Au(CN)_2^- \rightleftharpoons \ |-NR_2H^+Au(CN)_2^- + X^-$$

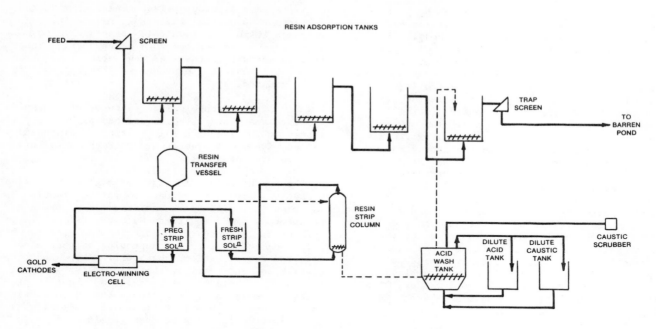

Figure 4. Conceptual flowsheet for gold recovery by the resin-in-column process.

Similar reactions occur for the extraction of silver from cyanide solutions. The weak base resins require protonation in order to extract anions. This occurs for pH values of less than 10, and, therefore, depending on the resin, some pH adjustment of the pregnant leach liquor might be required in order to obtain acceptable loadings on weak base resins.

Generally, the pH performance of these amine-type resins can be described by the plot shown in Figure 5.

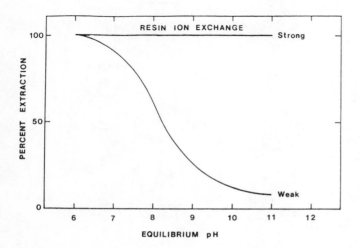

Figure 5. The effect of pH on the extraction of $Au(CN)_2^-$ by strong and weak base resins.

It is clear that the elution procedure for the RIC process will depend on the type of resins, i.e., weak or strong base. Weak base resin can be easily eluted by using a dilute caustic solution at ambient temperature. On the other hand, it is more difficult to elute the strong base resins. Researchers at MINTEK, South Africa, have been able to elute $Au(CN)_2^-$ from strong base resins using concentrated $Zn(CN)_4^{2-}$ solutions (Fleming and Nicol, 1981).

$$2\left|-NR_3^+Au(CN)_2^- + Zn(CN)_4^{2-} \rightleftharpoons (\left|-NR_3^+\right)_2Zn(CN)_4^{2-}\right.$$

$$+ 2Au(CN)_2^-$$

$$(\left|-NR_3^+\right)_2Zn(CN)_4^{2-} + 4H \rightleftharpoons 2\left|-NR_3^+X^- + ZnX_2 + 4HCN\right.$$

This procedure has proved effective but has the disadvantage that the resin needs to be regenerated using acid which destroys the zinc cyanide complex producing HCN gas which must then be readsorbed into NaOH to be returned to the process.

Solvent Extraction (SX)

This technology is still in its infancy, a suitable extractant having only recently been identified (Mooiman and Miller, 1983). Therefore many of the engineering aspects have not been studied and in this paper we shall present a rather simple flowsheet, incorporating the most common contactors, namely, mixer-settlers. This approach permits at least a first-order evaluation of the capital and operating costs for a gold solvent extraction plant. The conceptual flowsheet, shown in Figure 6, is described on the next page.

The pregnant leach solution from the heap will have to be filtered if the suspended solids content is too high, in order to avoid excessive solvent losses (by adsorption onto the solid particles). In addition, suspended solids promote phase disengagement problems and the formation of interfacial crud. The clarified solution is contacted with the organic phase in a series of two mixer-settlers with the organic phase flowing countercurrent to the aqueous phase. The mixer-settlers will have to be designed to allow organic recycle to achieve an organic:aqueous phase ratio of at least 1:1. The raffinate will have to be passed through a coalescence unit in order to limit the amount of entrained organic. A scavenging unit such as an activated-carbon bed might be used. The carbon would be periodically steam-stripped, thereby returning the organic to the circuit. In the solvent extraction circuit, the loaded organic from extraction is stripped with a 1-10% caustic solution at an organic-to-aqueous flow ratio of at least 10:1 in order to achieve the desired concentration of the gold values. The loaded strip solution is then passed to a conventional gold electrowinning cell.

It should be appreciated that the mixer-settler might not, in fact, be the best contactor for a gold solvent extraction circuit which requires high aqueous-to-organic flow ratios and very low organic losses. Among the contactors that could be considered are raining drop, centrifugal, or pulsed columns.

If contacting of the aqueous and organic phases proves to be difficult, another process option is to impregnate a porous polystyrene bead with the extractant, producing an impregnated resin, and to follow a resin-in-column (RIC) procedure. However, several advantages such as capacity, kinetics, selectivity, etc. over conventional RIC technology will have to be proved if this approach is to be adopted.

Many of the technological features of the gold SX process are described in another paper presented at the 1983 SME Fall Meeting (Mooiman and Miller, 1983). A brief summary of these features will be presented below.

The organic phase consists of a weak base amine whose basicity, with respect to gold extraction, has been increased by the addition of an organic phosphorous oxide modifier, such as TBP, all in an appropriate diluent. The gold-loading step can be performed at about pH 9.5 depending on the amine type and concentration, the modifier type and concentration, and possibly the diluent type. Small acid additions to the leach solution might be necessary in some cases to decrease the pH to a value in the range of pH 9-10 to maximize loading. The loading reaction for a secondary amine can be described as follows:

$$\overline{R_2NH} + H^+ + Au(CN)_2^- \leftrightarrows \overline{[R_2NH_2^+][Au(CN)_2^-]}$$

where R = C_{10}-C_{12} alkyl group. Good extraction is achieved at pH 9.5 even for feed solutions containing 10 ppm as shown in Table 3.

Stripping can be accomplished at pH values where the amine deprotonates, i.e., pH 12-13 or

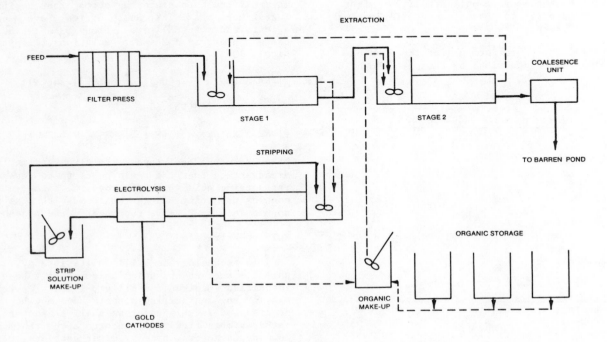

Figure 6. Conceptual flowsheet for gold recovery using solvent extraction.

Table 3. Gold Extraction from Cyanide Solution
with a Modified Secondary Amine

Equilibrium pH	Percent Extraction from 10 ppm Gold Solution
9.5	100.0
10.0	87.3
10.5	73.2
11.0	27.1
11.5	11.8

with a caustic solution of about 0.1-0.5%. The loading and stripping reaction rates are relatively fast, and therefore long contact times are not necessary. Excellent selectivity for gold over other metal cyanoanions present in alkaline cyanide leach solutions, e.g., $Fe(CN)_6^{3-}$, $Cu(CN)_3^{2-}$ etc. has been found which should allow for the production of a relatively pure gold product.

This technology has some interesting possibilities, and at the moment research and development activities are in progress.

Direct Electrowinning (DEW)

Electrowinning of gold according to the Zadra technique is practiced using rich eluates generated by the stripping of carbon from carbon adsorption circuits. In the case of heap leaching and as discussed in this paper, concentrated aurocyanide solutions can be produced by the following technologies:

* carbon-in-column
* resin-in-column
* solvent extraction

Paul et al. (1983) defined a "concentrated" aurocyanide solution as having gold concentrations ranging from 50 to 2000 ppm. At these concentrations gold can be electrodeposited onto encased stainless-steelwool cathodes. The direct electrowinning (DEW) of gold from dilute aurocyanide solution represents an emerging technology which has been suggested for heap leaching operations. Dilute aurocyanide solutions from heaps are defined as those having gold concentrations in the range of 1 to 10 ppm Au.

A direct electrowinning system, from which gold is recovered in the metallic state must have extended surface area electrodes and can be basically categorized as a flowthrough supported fiber electrode or as a particulate (packed-bed) electrode. In both cases, the electrodes are characterized as conductive material having extended surface areas (i.e. fiber or particulate carbon). The porous nature and the large active electrode

area serve to increase the mass transfer limiting currents and thus the rate of electrodeposition by

* reduction of boundary layer thickness as a result of the increased flow velocity imposed by the flow of solution through macro- and micro-channels of the electrode.

* increased specific surface area.

These factors may make it practical to electrowin metals at low concentrations from aqueous solution.

The DEW process for recovering precious metals from heap leaching circuits is illustrated in Figure 7. Leach solution from the heaps is clarified to remove suspended solids and is pumped to the electrolysis cells. Gold and silver are electrochemically deposited onto the extended surface area (ESA) cathodes and the barren solution is returned to the heaps after reagent make-up. The precious metal product can be recovered in several ways depending on the electrode system:

* For the particulate packed-bed electrode, the metal can be recovered by melting the carbon/precious metal particles in a furnace.

* For the supported, fibrous flowthrough electrodes, the metal can be removed by electrolytic stripping (i.e., the loaded cathode can be connected anodically and the metal deposited on a solid starting sheet cathode).

* Alternately, a chemical stripping approach can be used on either electrode system.

In the alkaline cyanide leach solution, the cathodic reactions of interest are:

$$Au(CN)_2^- + e \rightarrow Au + 2CN^- \qquad E° = -0.64v$$

$$Ag(CN)_2^- + e \rightarrow Ag + 2CN^- \qquad E° = -0.31v$$

$$O_2 + 2H_2O + 4e \rightarrow 4OH^- \qquad E° = 0.40v$$

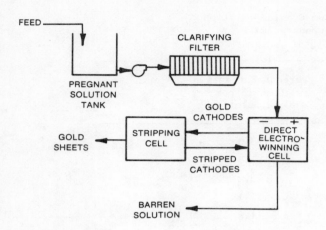

Figure 7. Conceptual flowsheet for gold
recovery by direct electrowinning.

As reported in Table 1 heap leach solutions may
contain significant concentrations of cuprocyanide
species which can undergo cathodic reduction as
well,

$$Cu(CN)_4^{3-} + e \rightarrow Cu + 4CN^- \quad E° = -0.75v$$

The reduction of the $Cu(CN)_2^-$ has a standard electrode potential of $E° = -0.43v$. In either case,
Au, Ag, and Cu will probably co-deposit at the
operating potentials.

Oxygen is generated at the anode and cyanide
ion is oxidized according to the following anodic
reaction:

$$CN^- + 2OH^- \rightarrow CNO^- + H_2O + 2e \quad E° = 0.97v$$

The cyanate ion reacts in the bulk solution to
yield CO_2 and NH_3 as follows:

$$CNO^- + 2H_2O \rightarrow CO_2 + NH_3 + OH^- \quad K = 9.1$$

Cyanide destruction during DEW can be avoided by
using a diaphragm electrolysis cell which isolates
the anodic compartment from the gold-bearing cyanide solution.

HSA Reactors Limited (1982) of Toronto, Canada,
manufacture and market a high-surface-area (HSA)
carbon-filter electrolysis system. This system
has been piloted at a heap-leaching operation in
Nevada. It is reported that existing systems can
accommodate solution flow rates of up to 400 gpm
and can achieve acceptable metal loadings from
precious metal solutions containing as little as
0.01 oz/ton.

Maslii and coworkers (1970) have examined the
application of extended surface area electrodes in
gold hydrometallurgy, operating cells since the
early 1970s. The carbon-graphite fiber version
contains 10-micron diameter threads giving a specific surface of 0.2 m^2/g. The capacity of these
cells is projected to reach 180 gpm.

Summary of Technological Features

1) Features of Conventional Technology

    Merrill Crowe Process
        Fast Reaction Kinetics
        Passivation-TSS, O_2, Poisons
        Low Selectivity
        Ease of Operation
        Good Accounting, Low Inventory

    Carbon in Column
        Slow Adsorption/Desorption Kinetics
        Excellent Recovery
        Low Sensitivity to TSS
        Fair Selectivity
        Carbon Transport-Regeneration
        Poor Accounting, High Inventory

2) Features of New Technology

    Resin in Column
        Intermediate Reaction Rates
        Insensitive to TSS
        Fair Selectivity
        Size/Density

    Solvent Extraction
        Fast Reaction Kinetics
        Sensitive to TSS
        Good Selectivity
        Organic Losses

    Direct Electrowinning
        Fast Reaction Kinetics
        Sensitive to TSS
        Fair Selectivity
        Low Capacity

ECONOMIC ANALYSIS

As detailed in the first part of this paper,
some of the new technologies, for example resin-
in-column (RIC), appear to offer considerable
technical advantage over the well-established
procedures such as Merrill-Crowe (MC). However,
it is interesting to examine how these new technologies compare economically, and this is the
objective of this section of the paper.

In order to present a fair comparison between
the various technologies, the capital and operating costs of only the gold recovery section were
calculated. Ore preparation, leaching, tailings
disposal, solution ponds, etc., were considered
the same for all processes. Also, the cost esti-
mation procedure was based on a theoretical feed
solution containing only gold. Silver recovery
was not considered. All calculations were based
on volumetric flowrates of pregnant leach liquor

and concentration of gold in the leach liquor. Solution flowrates in the 100–1000 gpm range were chosen, and two typical gold concentrations, 1 and 5 ppm, were used. These values should cover the wide range of operating conditions typically experienced in gold heap-leaching practice.

It is not intended that these capital and operating costs be definitive for any particular plant, but rather they serve as a basis of comparison of a particular processing strategy with respect to others. Any definitive cost study comparing process alternatives for a particular applications should of course involve the costing of the overall process, and naturally the extent of gold recovery would feature significantly in the calculation. However, recovery figures for new process options are often hard to come by and are not featured in our calculations. Unfortunately the costs for the DEW process were not available for inclusion in this report.

Capital Costs

The simplified flowsheets illustrated in Figures 2 to 5 were costed on the following basis: The capital cost estimates for the 100 and 1000 gpm extreme cases were obtained by costing the major items of equipment required for each process alternative. Engineering and construction costs were estimated. Piping, instrumentation, electrical, and ancillaries were factored from the cost of the major items of equipment. The cost of buildings and civils were excluded. The capital costs for the intermediate 500-gpm case were factored from the 1000-gpm costs using a cost exponent of 0.67, i.e., $(500/1000)^{0.67}$.

It should be appreciated that all these plants were sized and costed from the flowsheets. However, it should be noted that package processing units are available which are ideal for low flowrates and far less expensive than building a plant for a specific duty. For example, an MC unit that treats 50 gpm of leach solution can be obtained for approximately $25,000. The cost of these package units were not considered in this evaluation. Capital cost results are shown in Table 4.

Some interesting observations can be made from Figure 8 which shows capital cost versus solution flowrate for a 1 ppm Au feed. For all flowrates, the RIC option appears to be the most attractive

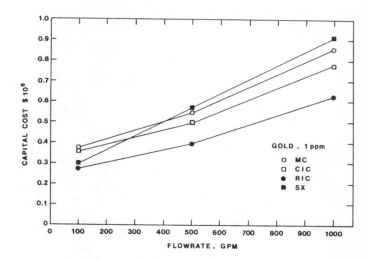

Figure 8. Capital cost as a function of solution flowrate at 1 ppm gold for different process alternatives.

as it has the lowest capital cost. It is less expensive than the CIC process because the RIC elution circuit does not require heat exchangers to heat the eluant and it does not require a regeneration kiln -- a particularly expensive item. At the lower flowrates (100 gpm), SX appears more economical than CIC or MC, but, at higher flowrates, the capital cost rapidly rises, making it economically unattractive.

In the CIC circuit some saving could be obtained if a vertical kiln were used instead of a horizontal kiln. The vertical kiln is approximately 30% less expensive and has a far lower operating cost. However, its efficiency and effect on carbon attrition is not known and will have to be determined. Considerable savings for both the RIC and CIC could be realized if a well-developed continuous ion exchange contactor were used instead of the discrete column arrangement as conventionally used in CIC circuits. Initial calculations indicate that overall capital cost savings of about 25% for both RIC and CIC could be obtained if a continuous contactor were installed. Some of the advantages that a continuous contactor would offer are:

Table 4. Capital Cost in 1983 U.S. Dollars for Different Gold Recovery Options

[Au]	Flowrate	CIC	MC	RIC	SX
1 ppm	100 gpm	360,000	364,000	283,000	309,000
1 ppm	1000 gpm	783,000	858,000	623,000	910,000
5 ppm	100 gpm	494,000	364,000	360,000	309,000
5 ppm	1000 gpm	1,046,000	858,000	820,000	910,000

* lower operating cost
* reduced plant area
* high extraction efficiencies
* simpler operation
* lower carbon/resin degradation
* high security for loaded carbon/resin
* lower carbon/resin inventory and reduced gold lock-up
* no dilution of process stream (due to the use of eductors)

Capital cost versus concentration of gold in the feed is depicted in Figure 9. It is interesting to note that the capital cost for both the RIC and CIC processes increase as the gold in the feed increases. As the gold concentration in the feed increases, the rate of gold loading on resin and carbon increases at a slower rate, and the carbon and resin will have to be moved faster through the circuit. Therefore, a larger stripping and/or regeneration section will be required, resulting in an increased capital cost. In the MC process, increasing gold concentration is simply handled by increasing the zinc addition rate. In solvent extraction the phase ratio could be decreased or the gold loading in the organic could be increased, except that the latter could increase gold losses via the entrained organic. The results in Figure 9 indicate that, at high gold concentrations (> 5 ppm), MC processing is the preferred procedure -- a conclusion that has been borne out in industrial practice.

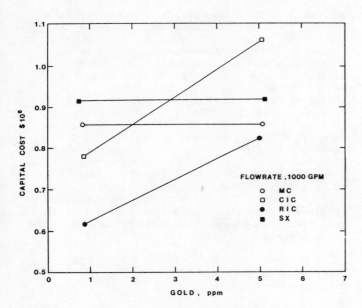

Figure 9. Capital cost as a function of solution concentration for different process alternatives at 1000 gpm.

Operating Costs

The basis for the calculation of operating costs is available from the authors on request.

The results from these detailed calculations of operating cost for each process are presented in Tables 5 through 8. The operating costs in $/1000 gal and $/annum are considered for a 1000 gpm plant and gold concentrations of 1 and 5 ppm. As can be seen in comparing carbon-in-column with Merrill Crowe, there is little difference in total operating costs for conventional technology and 1 ppm. However, a significant increase in carbon-in-column cost occurs for higher gold tenors. The reason for this cost increment is associated with the necessity to advance the carbon at a faster rate for higher concentrations and attendant increase in stripping and regeneration cost. However, all the carbon need not be regenerated on every cycle. The operating costs for a Merrill-Crowe process are particularly sensitive to zinc consumption which increases as the gold tenor rises.

Table 5. MERRILL-CROWE OPERATING COSTS

	1000 gpm -- 1 ppm		1000 gpm -- 5 ppm	
	$/1000 gal	$/year*	$/1000 gal	$/year*
Labor	0.40	201,600	0.40	201,600
Chemicals				
Zinc	0.10-0.20	75,600	0.20-0.40	151,200
Filter Aid	0.15-0.30	113,400	0.15-0.30	113,400
Power	0.10	50,400	0.10	50,400
Total	0.75-1.00	441,00	0.85-1.20	516,300

*Average cost per year

Table 6. CARBON-IN-COLUMN OPERATING COSTS

	1000 gpm -- 1 ppm		1000 gpm -- 5 ppm	
	$/1000 gal	$/year	$/1000 gal	$/year
Labor	.64	322,500	0.64	322,500
Chemicals				
Carbon	0.006	3,000	0.03	15,100
Eluate Make-Up	0.006	3,000	0.03	16,400
Steel Wool	0.001	500	0.005	2,500
Power				
Heating for Elution	0.03	15,100	0.14	70,500
E.W. Cell		300	0.004	2,000
Carbon Regeneration	0.20	100,800	0.40	201,600
Motors and Pumps	0.05	25,200	0.07	35,300
Total	0.926	470,400	1.314	665,900

Of the newer technologies, RIC appears particularly attractive. Solvent extraction, on the other hand, has a larger operating cost, a large component of which is contributed by the assumed organic loss. These organic losses and attendant operating costs could be improved if a coalescence unit were introduced into the circuit.

Table 7. RESIN-IN-COLUMN OPERATING COSTS

	1000 gpm — 1 ppm		1000 gpm — 5 ppm	
	$/1000 gal	$/year	$/1000 gal	$/year
Labor	0.64	322,500	0.64	322,500
Chemicals				
Resin	0.028	1,400	0.14	70,500
Eluate Make-Up	0.006	3,000	0.03	15,100
Steel Wool	0.001	500	0.005	2,500
pH Adjustment	0.02	10,100	0.02	10,100
Power				
E.W. Cell		300	0.004	2,000
Motors and Pumps	0.05	25,200	0.07	35,300
Total	0.746	363,000	0.908	458,000

Table 8. SOLVENT EXTRACTION OPERATING COSTS

	1000 gpm — 1 ppm		1000 gpm — 5 ppm	
	$/1000 gal	$/year*	$/1000 gal	$/year*
Labor	.064	322,500	0.64	322,500
Chemicals				
Filter Aid	0.15-0.30	113,400	0.15-0.30	113,400
Organic	0.83	418,000	0.83	418,300
Acid (pH adj.)	0.02	10,100	0.02	10,100
Strip Sol'n Make-Up	0.007	3,500	0.035	17,600
Steel Wool	0.001	500	0.001	500
Power				
E.W. Cell		300	0.004	2,100
Motors and Pumps	0.05	25,200	0.05	25,200
Total	1.69-1.848	893,500	1.73-1.89	909,700

*Average cost per year

Overall Cost Comparison

A convenient way to make an economic assessment of the process technologies is by considering the cumulative costs (capital plus yearly operating costs) that accrue during a period of operation. Such a comparison is presented in Figures 10 and 11. On these figures, the capital cost is represented by the intercept on the ordinate. The yearly operating costs are all in 1983 U.S. dollars.

The comparison indicates that at low gold concentration (1 ppm) there is little difference between MC and CIC in terms of overall cost. However, at increased gold concentrations (5 ppm), the cost for CIC is significantly greater than for MC. Therefore, of the conventional technologies, MC is the preferred method of gold recovery, especially at higher gold tenors.

In addition, this comparison points out that additional work will be required to make solvent extraction a competitive process alternative for heap leach solutions. It should be noted, however, that for gold concentrations exceeding 5

ppm, solvent extraction could become economically competitive. On the other hand, significant savings may be realized by the utilization of resin-in-column technology. The RIC process alternative offers an exciting process alternative for the recovery of gold from cyanide leach solutions.

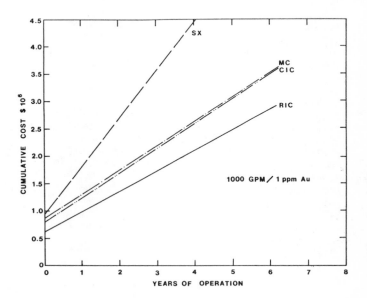

Figure 10. Cumulative cost for different process alternatives at 1000 gpm/1 ppm gold.

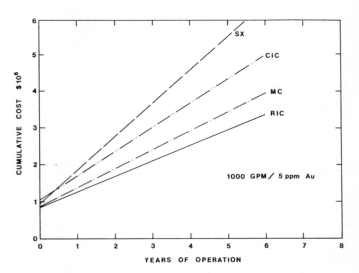

Figure 11. Cumulative cost for different process alternatives at 1000 gpm/5 ppm gold.

SUMMARY AND CONCLUSIONS

The potential for technology change in the recovery of gold from cyanide heap leach solution is high. This change could be via developments in conventional technology. In the case of the carbon-in-column process, improved reactor design (continuous contactors) and improved rate/selectivity of the adsorption/desorption reactions may provide for the advance in process technology. Probably the most signficant feature of carbon recovery technology is the essentially complete removal of gold from 1 ppm leach solutions. Electrolysis from the strip solution usually results in a satisfactory product quality for bullion production.

In the case of the Merrill-Crowe process, care must be taken to avoid the passivation and/or poisoning of zinc dust in order to achieve successful recovery from dilute heap leach solutions. The cementation reaction is fast, but the precipitation product quality can be low, especially for recovery from dilute solutions containing impurities. Electrolysis is not required in the Merrill-Crowe process. Although the processes differ significantly from a technology viewpoint, capital and operating costs are similar. It seems that the operating costs at 5 ppm gold would be somewhat higher for a carbon plant than for a Merrill-Crowe plant.

Development of new technology is in progress both in the U.S. and abroad. Some new process alternatives include resin-in-column, solvent extraction, and direct electrowinning. The most advanced of these alternatives is the resin-in-column process. Physical properties of the resin beads, selectivity and ease of stripping are areas of concern for the future development of the resin-in-column technology. Cost analyses suggest that such a process may have an advantage over conventional technology for gold recovery from heap leach solutions. New modified amines and other extractants have been discovered for selective solvent extraction of gold from alkaline cyanide solutions. With such extractants it should be possible to produce high-purity concentrated gold solutions. Engineering aspects of the solvent extraction system must be considered further. Solvent extraction seems to be competitive from a cost standpoint at concentrations exceeding 5 ppm. Direct electrowinning is possible with fiber electrodes and some pilot-scale programs are in progress to allow for better estimates of the potential of this technology.

Although many advances have been made in the past decade, exciting possibilities still exist for further improvement and innovation in gold recovery technology.

ACKNOWLEDGEMENT

MBM wishes to thank the Council for Mineral Technology, South Africa, for sponsorship of his graduate Studies.

REFERENCES

1. Chamberlain, P. G., and Pojar, M. G., 1981, "The Status of Gold and Silver Leaching Operations in the United States," Gold and Silver -- Leaching, Recovery, and Economics, W. J. Schlitt, W. C. Larson, and J. B. Hiskey, eds., SME-AIME, New York.

2. Clennell, 1915, "The Cyanide Handbook," McGraw-Hill, New York.

3. Davidson, R. J., and Veronese, V., 1979, "Further Studies on the Elution of Gold from Activated Carbon Using Water as the Eluant," J. S. Afr. Inst. Min. Metall., 79, 437, October.

4. "Chemistry of Carbon-in-Pulp and Resin-in-Pulp Processes," Paper presented at the Aust. Inst. Min. Metall. Meeting, Carbon-in-Pulp Technology for Extraction of Gold, Kalgoorlie, Australia (July).

5. Fleming, C. A., and Nicol, M. J., 1981, "Alternative Processes to Filtration: Carbon in Pulp and Resin in Pulp in the Metallurgical Industry," Procedings of Hydrometallurgy '81, Manchester, England.

6. Hendriksz, A. R., 1983, private communication, August.

7. Hickson, R. J., 1981, "Heap Leaching Practices at Ortiz Gold Mine, Santa Fe County, New Mexico," Presented at SME-AIME Fall Meeting, November 1981, SME Preprint No. 81-347.

8. HSA Reactors Limited, 1982, "Direct Precious-Metal Recovery System," HSA Bulletin DP-10-82, Ontario, Canada.

9. Jackson, D., 1982, "How Duval Transformed its Battle Mountain Properties from Copper to Gold Production," E and MJ, 95 (Oct.).

10. Lefler, C. A., 1981, "Leaching Practices at Smoky Valley Mine," Presented at AIME Annual Meeting, Chicago, February, 1981, SME Preprint No. 81-27.

11. Martin, J. P. Davidson, R. J., Duncanson, E., and Nkosi, N., 1976, "The Elution of Gold and Silver from Activated Carbon Using Organic Solvents and Reactivation of the Eluated Carbon Using Steam," Anglo-American Research Laboratories, Report No. 6.

12. Maslii, A. I., et al., 1970, "Using Electrodes with Extended Surfaces in Hydrometallurgy," Tsvetn, Met., 8, 40.

13. McDougall, G. J., Hancock, R. D., Nicol, M. J., Wellington, O. L., and Copperthwaite, R. G., 1980, "The Mechanism of the Absorption of Gold Cyanide on Activated Carbon," J.S. Afr., Inst. Min. Metall., 80, 344.

14.   McQuiston, F. W., and Shoemaker, R. S., 1981,
      <u>Gold and Silver Cyanidation Plant Practice</u>
      <u>Vol. II</u>, SME, AIME, New York.

15.   Mooiman, M. B., and Miller, J. D., 1981,
      "Selectivity Considerations in the Amine
      Solvent Extraction of Gold from Cyanide Solu-
      tions," SME Fall Meeting, Salt Lake City,
      October.

16.   Mooiman, M. B., and Miller, J. D., 1983, "The
      Solvent Extraction of Gold from Aurocyanide
      Solutions," Proceedings of ISEC '83, Denver.

17.   Muir, D. M., and Hinchcliffe, W., 1981, "Mur-
      doch MCRU Solvent Process for Desorption of
      Gold from Activated Carbon," Mineral Chem-
      istry Research Unit Report (December).

18.   Paul, R. L., Filmer, A. O., and Nicol, M. J.,
      1983, "The Recovery of Gold from Concentrated
      Aurocyanide Solutions," <u>Hydrometallurgy Re-</u>
      <u>search, Development and Plant Practice</u>, eds.,
      K. Osseo-Asare and J. D. Miller, TMS-AIME,
      New York.

19.   Zadra, J. B., Engel, A. K., and Heinen,
      H. J., 1952, "A Process for Recovery of Gold
      from Activated Carbon by Leaching and Elec-
      trolysis," U.S.B.M. Report #4843.

Chapter 11

EXPERIMENTAL STATISTICAL OPTIMIZATION OF ZINC PRECIPITATION PARAMETERS

Omar A. Muhtadi
Pegasus' Gold Corp.
P.O. Box 313
Zortman, Montana 59546

ABSTRACT

Experimental statistical designs were used at Zortman Mining Company's, Zortman, Montana, heap-leach operation to establish functional relationships between key operating parameters and gold/silver recoveries. Zinc feed rate, lead feed rate, and vacuum (CFM/gpm) account for 64% and 67% of the attainable gold and silver recoveries, respectively.

Surface response graphs of the resulting polynomials were plotted. These graphs were used to optimize Zortman's Merrill-Crowe precipitation process.

INTRODUCTION

The recovery of gold and silver from a pregnant solution using the Merrill-Crowe zinc precipitation process is usually dependent on key parametric variables. This paper presupposes the existence of the conditions necessary to precitate gold, and thence, introduces a method to mathematically optimize gold recovery using a three-level Plackett-Burman screening design and a corner-plus-star-points design.

Preparation for Analysis

For a particular leaching application, it is necessary to determine which parameters are the most influential on gold recovery. Based upon the number of these major variables, tests are then performed to optimize each one for gold recovery. Zortman Mining Company runs a heap-leach mine in Zortman, Montana. The gold and silver are recovered from the pregnant solution using a Merrill-Crowe precipitation process.

A series of tests were performed at the Zortman Plant site in order to optimize gold recovery. The tests were executed under normal production conditions. All of the data was obtained by altering feed-rates and flows during plant operation. Sufficient time was allowed between different tests such that a realistic response would be obtained at a steady state, and such that the normal production of the plant would not be adversely affected in the case where recovery dropped.

It is felt that in order to obtain the most realistic results, bench-scale and pilot-scale tests would not suffice.

Study Objectives

To date, few study results have been published on the statistical optimization of a Merrill-Crowe recovery process. This study was designed specifically for filling this gap.

THEORY OF EXPERIMENTAL DESIGN

The literature on the theory of statistical design is extensive, however, Box, Hunter, and Hunter (1978) provide a good overview of the subject. They indicate the fact that fractional factorial designs of the type used here, are extremely useful for the purpose of measuring the effects of one or more variables on a response. In exploring a functional relationship, it might appear reasonable at first to adopt a comprehensive approach in which the entire range of every factor was investigated. However, when runs can be made in successive groups, this is an inefficient way to organize experimental programs. (Box et al. 1978)

At the outset of a design, the experimenter selects a fixed number of "levels" for each number of variables and then runs experiments with all possible combinations. A display of levels to be run in a design is called a design matrix. Table I shows the design matrix for a Plackett-Burman

three-level design with four variables.

Without benefit of complete theoretical development, it can be stated that the Plackett-Burman design is used to establish linear relationships between the variables and the response, while the corner-plus-star-points design is then a further refinement establishing linear, quadratic and two factor interactions. Table II shows the generalized design matrix of corner-plus-star-points design for three variables. See Marske (1970), Hunter (1976), and Daniel (1976) for further information.

Table I. Plackett-Burman Design Matrix (for 4 variables)

	Variable			
Test	x_1	x_2	x_3	x_4
1	+	+	+	−
2	+	+	−	+
3	+	−	+	−
4	−	+	−	−
5	+	−	−	+
6	−	−	+	+
7	−	+	+	+
8	−	−	−	−
9	0	0	0	0
10	0	0	0	0

The 'levels' of the variables are coded by zeroes, minus and plus signs.

Table II. Composite Star Design Matrix (5-levels; 3 independent variables)

		Variable			
	Test	x_1	x_2	x_3	
Corner Points	1	+	+	+	
	2	+	+	−	
	3	+	−	+	
	4	+	−	−	
	5	−	+	+	
	6	−	+	−	
	7	−	−	+	
	8	−	−	−	
Star Points	9	+2	0	0	
	10	−2	0	0	
	11	0	+2	0	(+2, −2 for
	12	0	−2	0	5-levels)
	13	0	0	+2	
	14	0	0	−2	
Center Points	15	0	0	0	(replicated
	16	0	0	0	twice)

Calculation of Main Effects

The initial Plackett-Burman is used primarily to establish the most important variables affecting the response. After determining this information, further tests can then be executed with these 'primary' variables.

There are two methods commonly used for calculating effects. The easiest to implement is the averaging of individual measures of effects. What is meant by the effect of a factor is the change in the response as one moves from the − to the + version of that factor.

The main effect for each of the variables is defined as the difference between two averages:

$$\text{main effect} = \bar{y}_+ - \bar{y}_- \qquad (1)$$

where $\bar{y}_+$ is the average response for the plus level of the variable $\bar{y}_-$ is the average response for the minus level.

It can be seen from equation (1) that with this method of calculating effects, the zero level is not accounted for. Computer statistical methods allow the inclusion of the zero-level. These methods use standard statistical tests of correlation with each variable, and also the combined effect with all the variables simultaneously included. As the method used here is quite basic, no further development is needed. Suffice it to say that any statistical text covering multiple linear regression would be a good source of more information.

Calculation of Interaction Effects

Whenever the analysis with the corner-plus-star-points design is made, quadratic and variable interaction may be investigated.

Very often, variables are not related to the response by a simple linear relationship. It is seen that the square or even the cube of certain variables affect the response. In the case where there is factor interaction - ie. two or more variables together affect the response - then a measure of this interaction is supplied by the difference between the average effect of one variable versus the effect of the other. For example, if x_1 and x_2 affect the response y, then by convention, half the difference is called the x_1 by x_2 interaction or, in symbols, the $(x_1 x_2)$ interaction (Box et al., 1978).

Once all of the above analysis is completed, then an equation can be written to describe the functional relationships between the variables and the response. Optimization of this equation will then lead to the desired response value. The generated recovery equations are plotted on response surface graphs. This allows the behavior of a response to be "seen" on a contour map. (See Box et al., 1978).

METHODS AND CALCULATION

Preliminary Screening

Initially, four operating variables were picked from experience as those markedly affecting gold and silver recovery.

The four variables picked were:
1. Zinc feed rate in grams/minute
2. Lead acetate feed rate in ml/minute
3. Turbidity in NTU
4. Cubic feet per minute vacuum/gallons per minute solution flow rate (CFM/gpm)

The CFM is a constant for a given vacuum pump, and in this case, it is 600. Table III shows the −1, 0, and +1 levels chosen for the variables.

Table III. Factor Values for the Initial Screening.

Factor	−1	0	+1
Zinc	40	100	160
Lead	4	16	36
Turbidity	0.5	1.00	1.5
Vacuum (CFM/gpm)	0.75	0.55	0.43

The Plackett-Burman screening matrix was constructed using the values given in Table III. Shown in Table IV is the design matrix, including the responses.

Table IV. Plackett-Burman Design Matrix.

	Variables in Orig. Units*				Recovery	
Run(a)	T	Zn	Pb(b)	V	Ag %	Au %
1	1.5	160	36	0.75	79.00	99.31
2	1.5	160	4	0.43	96.84	84.03
3	1.5	40	36	0.75	87.73	17.36
4	0.5	160	4	0.75	83.53	95.41
5	1.5	40	4	0.43	97.40	13.19
6	0.5	40	36	0.43	75.99	84.71
7	0.5	160	36	0.43	86.96	93.88
8	0.5	40	4	0.75	99.58	62.35
9	1.0	100	16	0.55	99.68	99.20
10	1.0	100	16	0.55	99.68	99.20

* T=Turbidity (NTU); Zn=Zinc (gms/min); Pb=Lead (ml/min); V=Vacuum (CFM/gpm)
(a) The order of these runs was randomized. The first five were obtained in the order 1, 5, 3, 2, 4, and the next five in the order 9, 10, 7, 6, and 8.
(b) Lead is added as a solution of 750 g Pb(NO$_3$)$_2$ per gallon of distilled water. Therefore, there was 0.124 grams of lead/ml.

Table IV now supplied sufficient information in order to determine which, if any, of the four factors is relatively unimportant in the recovery of gold and silver.

The first method investigated for testing factor 'importance' is the average effect method. (See equation (1).)

Turbidity Effect on Gold (from Table IV):

$$T = \frac{99.31 + 84.03 + 17.36 + 13.19}{4} -$$

$$\frac{95.41 + 84.71 + 93.88 + 62.35}{4} =$$

$$53.47 - 84.09 = -30.62 \qquad (2)$$

Similar computations were made to obtain the rest of the results on Table V. Also shown are the linear correlations of each factor on gold and silver recovery.

Table V. Main Effects and Correlations.

Factor	Au Effect	Ag Effect	AuR^2*	AgR^2
Turbidity	-30.62	3.73	0.24	0.01
Zinc	48.78	- 3.60	0.29	0.13
Lead	10.08	-11.92	0.05	0.19
Vacuum	16.33	3.41	0.03	0.07

* R^2 = (Linear correlation)^2

Based on the results given, the following observations are made:

1. The most negative effect seen is that of turbidity on gold recovery, at -30.62.
2. The most insignificant correlation is that of turbidity on silver recovery, at 0.01.
3. With the main interest being gold recovery, all the other variables supply a positive effect.

Therefore, it is concluded that for the secondary design study, the only factor that could reasonably be dropped out is the turbidity.

Secondary Tests

Table VI shows the -2, -1, 0, +1, and +2 levels chosen. It must be noted at this time that although the experiment was not designed as such, the author believes that the values should have been chosen such that they are symmetrical about 0; that being a more rigorous approach.

Table VI. Factor Values for Secondary Analysis.

Factor	-2	-1	0	+1	+2
(x_1)Zinc	40	70	100	130	160
(x_2)Lead	4	10	16	24	36
(x_3)(CFM/gpm)	0.43	0.50	0.55	0.60	0.75

In this case, the flow was decreased going from the -2 to the +2 levels such that the ratio of (600/flow) would increase.

Shown on Table VII is the complete set of data used for the second part of analysis. Included are columns with quadratic and factor interaction values.

Correlation calculations were performed between each column in Table VII and gold or silver recoveries. The columns found to have the highest R^2 values were incorporated together, and a simultaneous regression coefficient was calculated between these and gold/silver recoveries.

A lowerbound value of R^2 had to be calculated. Any R^2 value below that was not included in the multiple regression equation. By definition, for any random variable,

$$R^2 = \frac{1}{n-1} \tag{3}$$

where, n = number of data points.

In this case, where there are 16 observations,

$$R^2 = \frac{1}{(16-1)} = \underline{0.0666} \tag{4}$$

Therefore, all variables whose R^2 was higher than 0.066 were included in the resulting polynomial.

RESULTS AND DISCUSSION

Standard computer programs were used to run a step-wise correlation on the data. Table VIII is a listing of R^2 for variables of importance. Again, those factors with $R^2 < 0.066$ are omitted.

Table VIII. Table of Linear Correlations.

Gold Recovery Factor	R^2	Silver Recovery Factor	R^2
x_1	0.339	$x_3{}^2$	0.275
$x_1 x_3$	0.297	x_3	0.240
$x_1{}^2$	0.271	$x_1 x_2$	0.155
$x_2 x_3$	0.093	$x_1 x_3$	0.123
x_2	0.087	x_2	0.070

Simultaneous regression analysis was then performed on the factors. The following equations were obtained:

Gold Recovery,

$$\hat{y} = -10.65 - 0.722x_1 + 4.74(x_1 x_3) - 0.007x_1{}^2$$

$$- 29.84(x_2 x_3) + 15.38x_2 \tag{5}$$

and Silver Recovery,

$$\hat{y} = 54.51 - 196.48x_3{}^2 + 149.82x_3 - 0.016(x_1 x_2)$$

$$+ 0.42(x_1 x_3) + 1.42x_2 \tag{6}$$

where $\hat{y}$ = estimated gold or silver recovery.

The simultaneous regression coefficients, R^2, were 0.644 and 0.670 for gold and silver respectively. The quantitative translation of the R^2 values, is that 64.4% of the gold recovery, (and 67.0% of the silver recovery) are described by x_1, x_2 and x_3 according to equations (3) and (4). The remaining 35.6% of recovery is then described

Table VII. Data and Results Listing for Corner-plus-star-points Design.

		Design Matrix						Calculated Second Order Factors				
Run	x_1	x_2	x_3	R_{Au}	R_{Ag}	x_1^2	x_2^2	x_3^2	$(x_1 x_2)$	$(x_1 x_3)$	$(x_2 x_3)$
1	130	24	0.5	98.91	87.80	16900	576	0.25	3120	65	12
2	130	24	0.6	99.64	86.60	16900	576	0.36	3120	78	14.4
3	130	10	0.5	99.64	99.80	16900	100	0.25	1300	65	5
4	130	10	0.6	99.64	99.80	16900	100	0.36	1300	78	6
5	70	24	0.5	75.55	99.80	4900	576	0.25	1680	35	12
6	70	24	0.6	7.30	99.80	4900	576	0.36	1680	42	14.4
7	70	10	0.5	99.04	99.43	4900	100	0.25	700	35	5
8	70	10	0.6	99.04	99.43	4900	100	0.36	700	42	6
9	160	16	0.55	95.62	99.80	25600	256	0.30	2560	88	8.8
10	40	16	0.55	36.13	94.80	1600	256	0.30	640	22	8.8
11	100	36	0.55	86.13	98.80	10000	1296	0.30	3600	55	19.8
12	100	4	0.55	96.15	99.43	10000	16	0.30	400	55	2.2
13	100	16	0.43	76.64	99.40	10000	256	0.19	1600	43	6.88
14	100	16	0.75	94.23	85.04	10000	256	0.56	1600	75	12
15	100	16	0.55	87.23	99.40	10000	256	0.30	1600	55	8.8
16	100	16	0.55	96.72	99.40	10000	256	0.30	1600	55	8.8

KEY: x_1 = Zinc (gms/min) R_{Au} = gold recovery
     x_2 = Lead (cc/min)
     x_3 = CFM/gpm R_{Ag} = silver recovery

by a number of other variables, not tested with this design.

It is well worth mentioning that in all probability, and under ideal lab conditions, a larger value for the regression coefficient may have been obtained. Due to the fact that the experiments were run under production plant conditions, the author feels confident that the results obtained are statistically significant.

Response Surface Plots

In order to better "see" the trends of equations (5) and (6), response surface plots are made of them. In both equations, zinc feed rate, and CFM/gpm, are very important parameters. Therefore, response surface plots are drawn in each case for x_1 versus x_3, at three separate levels of the lead feed rate, x_2. Complete coverage of this method is presented in Box et al. (1978).

Figures 1 through 6 are the response surface plots. All the contours were drawn through computer fitted points -- ie. the polynomial was evaluated at those values to obtain the recoveries.

The points evaluated in the experiment are shown by the symbol ▲, with the recovery values written alongside. It is within the region bound by those points that rigorous interpolation is allowed. (These regions are shown shaded at the 0 levels for the gold and silver plots.)

An Application Example

The following example is illustrated in Figure 2.

At the beginning of the run, the zinc feed rate is 80 gm/min, and the gallons per minute going through the Zortman Plant is 1200. Therefore, the ratio CFM/gpm = 600/1200 = 0.50. The lead feed rate at this time is 16 cc/min (ie. $x_2 = 0$ from Table VI). It is seen that the gold recovery is about 80-81%.

Zortman Mining now would like to change operating conditions within the plant such that their gold recovery approches 100%. The most direct method is to follow a line from point A to point B. Point B lies on the upperbound 100% recovery. According to the surface plot, the zinc feed rate would have to increase to 114 gm/min, and the CFM/gpm ratio would have to increase to 0.62, i.e. the flow would have to decrease to 968 gpm.

It is interesting to note that Figure 2 shows that for a given vacuum pump (at a constant CFM), there is a maximum flow allowed through the plant for 100% recovery. The point is shown as C, with a flow of about 1100 gpm. Theoretically, therefore, in order for the Zortman Plant to be able to run a higher gpm, a larger vacuum pump would have to be installed.

Other figures are similarly used for different levels of lead feed rate, and depending on whether silver or gold recovery is to be maximized.

SUMMARY AND CONCLUSIONS

Merrill-Crowe zinc precipitation was optimized at the Zortman Mining Plant site using a statistical experimental approach. By running a series of tests according to Plackett-Burman and corner-plus-star-points designs, equations (5) and (6) were determined. These equations describe the relationship between operating parameters and gold/silver recoveries.

The following are general conclusions regarding this procedure:

1) The method presented is a statistical procedure, and could be used for the optimization of other extraction techniques, such as C.I.P. and carbon adsorption.
2) Gold and silver recoveries are dependent on three major variables; zinc feed rate, lead feed rate, and the ratio CFM/gpm.
3) These three parameters account for 64.4% and 67.0% of the gold and silver recoveries respectively, at Zortman.
4) Gold and silver recoveries are related via quadratic equations to the above parameters.
5) Surface response plots of the optimizing equations are used to graphically improve gold/silver recovery in an operating plant.
6) On the response surface plots, the gold equation describes a hyperbolic paraboloid, while the silver equation describes a hyperboloid.

ACKNOWLEDGMENT

The author wishes to acknowledge Pegasus Gold Ltd. for allowing the results of this study to be published. Sincere thanks go to Mr. Dan O'Donnell of Newmont Exploration Ltd. His help and guidance are immeasurably appreciated.

REFERENCES

Box, George E.P. et. at., 1978, "Statistics for Experimenters" John Wiley and Sons, New York.

Box, George E.P., and Wilson, K.B., 1951, "On the Experimental Attainment of Optimum Conditions," J. Roy. Stat. Soc, Ser. B, 13, 1.

Cochran, W.G., and Cox, G.M., 1957, "Experimental Designs" 2nd Ed., New York: John Wiley and Sons, Inc.

Davies, O.L., 1963, "The Design and Analysis of Industrial Experiments" New York: Hafner Publishing Co.

Daniel, C., 1976, "Applications of Statistics to Industrial Experimentation" Wiley.

Federer, W.T., 1955, "Experimental Designs, Theory and Application" New York: The Macmillan Co.

Fisher, R.A., 1957, "The Design of Experiments," 4th Ed., New York: Hafner Publishing Co.

Freund, J.E., 1971, "Mathematical Statistics," 2nd Ed., Englewood Cliffs, N.J.: Prentice-Hall, Inc.

Hicks, C.R., 1965, "Fundamental Concepts in the Design of Experiments" New York: Holt, Rinehart & Winston, Inc.

Hogg, R.V. and Craig, A.T., 1970, "Introduction to Mathematical Statistics" 3rd Ed., New York: The Macmillan Co.

Lipson, C. and Sheth, N.J., 1973, "Statistical Design and Analysis of Engineering Experiments" New York: McGraw-Hill Book Co.

Marske, D.M., 1970, "High-rate, Fine-mesh of Screening of Combined Wastewater Flows," J. Water Pollut. Control Fed., 42, 1476.

Scheffe, H., 1959, "The Analysis of Variance" New York: John Wiley and Sons, Inc.

Snedecor, G.W. and Cochran, W.G., 1967, "Statistical Methods" 6th Ed., Ames, Iowas" Iowa University Press.

Smith, H. and Rose, A., 1963, "Subjective Responses in Process Investigation," Ind. Eng. Chem., 55, 25.

Yates, F., 1937, "The Design and Analysis of Factorial Experiments" Bulletin 35 - Imperial Bureau of Soil Science, Harpenden, Herts, England.

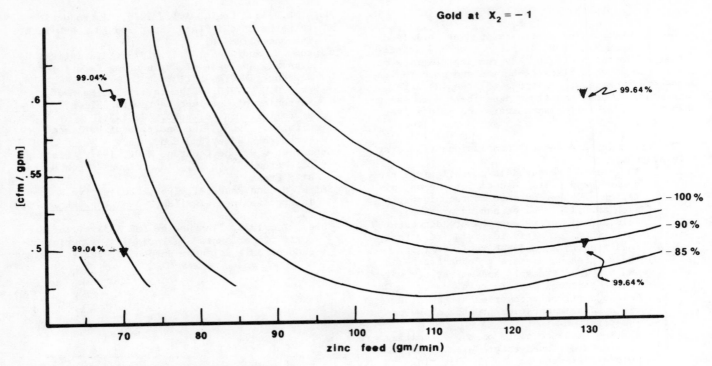

Figure 1. Fitted contours of Eq. 5

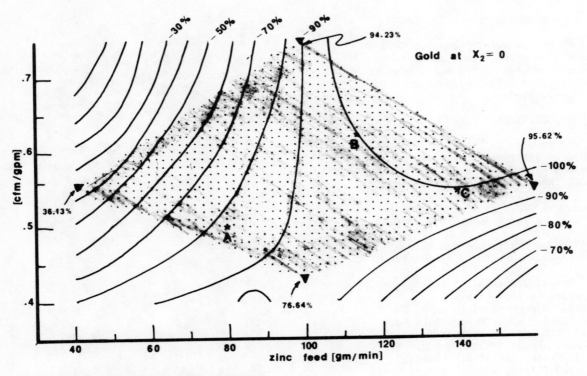

Figure 2. Fitted contours of Eq. 5

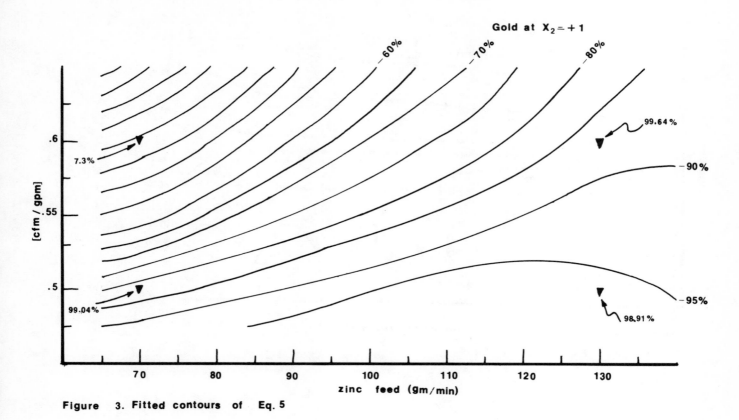

Figure 3. Fitted contours of Eq. 5

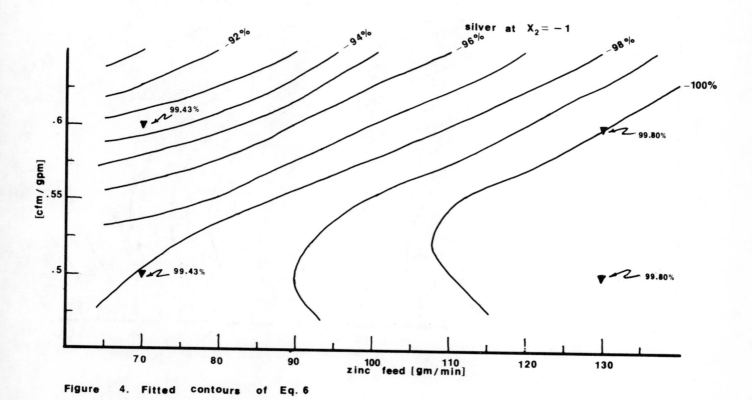

Figure 4. Fitted contours of Eq. 6

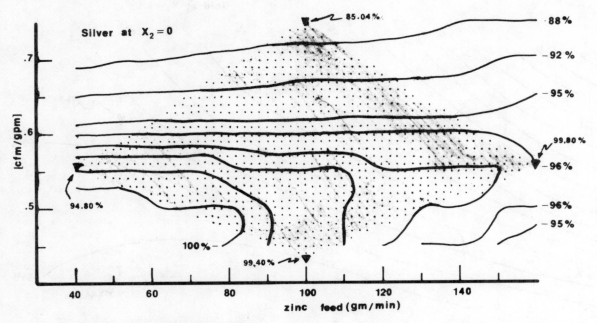

Figure 5. Fitted contours of Eq. 6

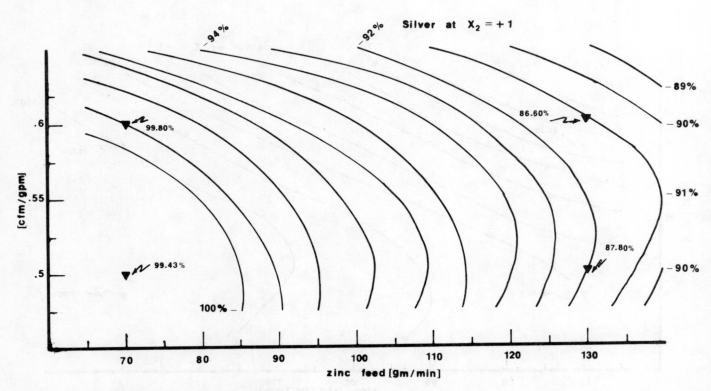

Figure 6. Fitted contours of Eq. 6

Chapter 12

MERCURY REMOVAL FROM
GOLD CYANIDE LEACH SOLUTION

W.L. Staker
W.W. Simpson
R.G. Sandberg
U.S. Department of the Interior
Bureau of Mines
Salt Lake City, Utah

ABSTRACT

The Bureau of Mines investigated selective extraction of Au and Ag from a low-grade Au ore containing Hg. Gold and silver were extracted from the ore in cyanide slurries, and Hg extraction was suppressed with sodium or calcium sulfide. Maximum Au extraction and minimum Hg extraction were obtained using solutions containing 0.34 lb NaCN/ton of solution. Increasing the cyanide concentration increased Hg extraction without increasing Au extraction. Mercury extraction from the ore was suppressed with 0.5 to 2.9 lb CaS/lb Hg in the ore. Gold-to-mercury ratios of 100:1 to 400:1 were obtained in the leach solution, and on the activated carbon in a CIP circuit.

INTRODUCTION

During the past few years, several low-grade gold ore deposits containing mercury have been developed and are being processed by cyanidation to recover precious metals. These ores usually have less than 15 ppm mercury content. During cyanidation, 10 to 30% of the mercury is extracted along with gold and silver. Gold, silver, and mercury are adsorbed from the leach solution by activated carbon in a carbon-in-pulp (CIP) circuit. The metals are stripped from carbon with hot solutions of sodium hydroxide-sodium cyanide or alcohol-sodium hydroxide-sodium cyanide. The metals are recovered from the strip solution by electrolysis onto steel wool cathodes (Laxen 1979).[1]

[1] Names and dates in parentheses refer to items in the list of references at the end of this report.

Cathodes are retorted under vacuum at 650-700° C to remove mercury prior to smelting gold to Dore bars (Thorndycraft 1982). Generally, small amounts of mercury extracted from the ore are more of a nuisance than an economic asset and require additional process steps for mercury separation from gold and silver. In addition, mercury vapor may cause health hazards in the electrowinning, the retorting, and the carbon reactivation areas. Reactions representing gold and mercury extraction with cyanide (Potter 1978) are -

$$2 Au + 4 CN^- + O_2 + 2H_2O \rightarrow 2 Au(CN)_2^-$$
$$+ 2 OH^- + H_2O_2$$

$$2 Au + 4 CN^- + H_2O_2 \rightarrow 2 Au(CN)_2^- + 2 OH^-$$

$$Hg^{2+} + 4 CN^- \rightarrow Hg(CN)_4^{2-}$$

$$2 Hg + 8 CN^- + O_2 + 2 H_2O \rightarrow 2 Hg(CN)_4^{2-}$$
$$+ 4 OH^- \tag{1}$$

Mine operations uninterested in recovering mercury may find it advantageous to selectively extract precious metals and leave mercury in the discarded tails. Rejecting mercury in the tails as solid mercury sulfide would eliminate mercury vapor hazards in the plant area. The Bureau of Mines has been investigating methods for selectively extracting gold and silver with the use of sulfides to suppress mercury extraction. Sulfides that are soluble in cyanide solutions could be used for this purpose. As early as 1915, it was known that sulfides of gold, silver, iron, zinc, and copper were soluble in a cyanide solution, and silver sulfide was used to precipitate mercury from a cyanide solution (Clennell 1915). Silver, iron and zinc sulfides have been used to precipitate mercury from filtered gold cyanide solutions (Flynn 1981). Silver sulfide would tie up considerable precipitant in recycle, and all excess precipitant would need to

be recovered. Iron, zinc, and copper sulfides are undesirable because they would consume cyanide in the formation of complex cyanides, which would (Door 1950) adsorb on activated carbon and lower the loading capacity for gold.

Mercury extraction can be somewhat controlled by decreasing the cyanide content of the leach solution. However, it would be difficult to control mercury solubility and obtain good precious metal recovery by regulating cyanide concentration. In this investigation, calcium and sodium sulfides were studied as mercury extraction suppressants in cyanide solution. These reagents are relatively inexpensive and are not harmful to the CIP recovery of precious metals. Reactions representing mercury precipitation with calcium and sodium sulfide are -

$$Hg(CN)_4^{2-} + CaS \rightarrow \underline{HgS} + Ca^{2+} + 4 CN^-$$

$$Hg(CN)_4^{2-} + Na_2S \rightarrow \underline{HgS} + 2Na^+ + 4 CN^- \tag{2}$$

MATERIALS AND EQUIPMENT

Ore used in this investigation was obtained from a gold mining operation in northern Nevada. The ore body is described as an oxidized hydrothermal deposit with gold finely disseminated as micrometer-sized particles. Host rock of limestone-siltstone has silicified to jasperoid and partly weathered to clay. The ore was crushed and wet-ballmilled to give 90% passing through a 200-mesh screen. The ground ore was dried at room temperature and utilized in leach tests. No specific gold or mercury minerals were identified by microscopic analysis. Chemical analysis of the ore is given in Table No. 1.

Table No. 1

CHEMICAL ANALYSIS OF ORE

Element	Analysis
Aluminum	3.2%
Arsenic	0.12%
Barium	0.077%
Cadmium	0.005%
Calcium	8.9%
Chromium	0.01%
Cobalt	0.01%
Copper	0.008%
Gold	0.096 oz per ton
Iron	4.00%
Lead	0.01%
Magnesium	0.64%
Manganese	0.11%
Mercury	17.00 ppm
Molybdenum	0.02%
Nickel	<0.01%
Phosphorus	0.18%
Silicon	>23.00%
Silver	0.056 oz per ton
Thorium	<0.01%
Titanium	<0.15%
Zinc	0.026%

Reagent-grade chemicals were used in the investigation. Mercury, gold and silver analyses and distribution were determined by atomic adsorption spectrophotometry and radioisotopes, using a Tracor Northern TN-1710 gamma counter.[2]

---
[2]Reference to specific trade names or manufacturers does not imply endorsement by the Bureau of Mines.

Isotopes used were gold 195, mercury 203, and silver 110m.

EXPERIMENTAL PROCEDURE, RESULTS AND DISCUSSION

Standard Test Method

A standard method of performing leach tests was developed for determining the effectiveness of gold-mercury separations in cyanide solutions using sulfides to suppress mercury solubility. Ground ore, sodium cyanide, and calcium oxide were added to distilled water in open beakers. The solution was mechanically stirred, and air was bubbled through the slurry. Comparative tests were run by rolling the slurry in closed bottles containing 50 to 400 ml of air above the slurry. After a 24-hr leach, the solutions and residues were assayed. Table 2 shows gold recoveries of about 90% were nearly the same in the bottle tests and in the open beaker, and were independent of solids and cyanide content used. The bottle, more convenient than the beaker, was selected as the standard test method.

Effect Of Sodium Cyanide Concentration on Gold and Mercury Extraction

Standard bottle tests were run to determine gold and mercury extraction with increasing cyanide concentration in the leach solution. One-hundred grams of test ore were leached in 150 ml of solution containing from 0.042 gram sodium cyanide per liter (0.084 lb per ton) to 0.5 gram sodium cyanide per liter (1.0 lb per ton) and 0.06 gram calcium oxide (1.2 lb per ton). After a 24-hr leach, the solutions and residues were assayed. Table No. 3 and Figure I show that maximum gold extraction was obtained with 0.17 gram sodium cyanide per liter (0.34 lb per ton) and above. Using higher cyanide concentrations than necessary to obtain maximum precious metal extraction increases mercury and tramp metal extraction and consumes greater quantities of cyanide.

Table No. 3

GOLD AND MERCURY EXTRACTION WITH INCREASING CYANIDE CONCENTRATION

Sodium cyanide concentration		Extraction, percent	
gram/l	lb/ton	Gold	Mercury
0.042	0.084	67.5	0.5
0.085	0.17	87.9	4.7
0.17	0.34	90.9	12.0
0.50	1.00	91.2	27.0

Table No. 2

COMPARATIVE EXTRACTION OF GOLD AND MERCURY IN OPEN BEAKER AND CLOSED BOTTLES

Test Method	Weight of ore used, gram	Volume of solution used, ml	Solids in slurry, percent	Reagent addition				Recovery percent	
				NaCN		CaO			
				gram/l	lb/ton	gram	lb/ton	Gold	Mercury
Beaker	50	600	7.7	2.17	4.3	0.1	4.0	87.4	26.7
Beaker	500	625	44.0	2.45	4.9	1.0	4.0	85.3	23.0
Bottle	50	600	7.7	2.17	4.3	0.1	4.0	89.9	21.3
Bottle	100	150	40.0	0.17	0.34	0.06	1.2	91.0	12.0
Bottle	500	750	40.0	0.17	0.34	0.625	2.5	90.3	10.0

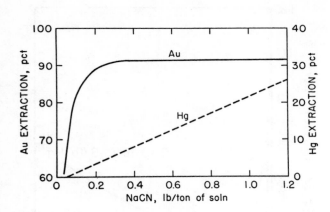

FIGURE I. GOLD AND MERCURY EXTRACTION WITH
INCREASING CYANIDE CONCENTRATION

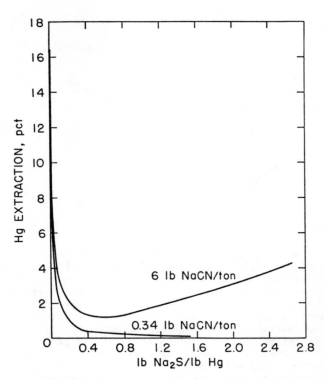

FIGURE II. EFFECT OF SODIUM SULFIDE AND SODIUM
CYANIDE CONCENTRATION ON MERCURY EXTRACTION

Mercury Removal by Sulfide Precipitation

Suppression of Mercury Extraction With Sodium Sulfide. Standard bottle leach tests were conducted to determine selective extraction of gold and silver when applying sodium sulfide to suppress mercury extraction in a cyanide solution. A test series was performed to assess the effect of increasing concentrations of sodium sulfide on mercury extraction in a solution containing 0.17 gram of sodium cyanide per liter (0.34 lb per ton of solution). A second test series was conducted with a solution containing 3 grams of sodium cyanide per liter (6.0 lb per ton of solution). One-hundred grams of ore were leached in 150 ml of cyanide solution and 2.5 lb calcium oxide per ton of ore added to maintain protective alkalinity. After 24 hr of leaching, a sodium sulfide solution was added to precipitate dissolved mercury. The sodium sulfide was added in the amounts of moles sodium sulfide per mole mercury (lb sodium sulfide per lb mercury) in the ore. The slurry was rolled for another 1/2 hr and filtered. Figure II and Table No. 4 show less than 1% of the mercury is solubilized by addition of 0.38 to 1.5 lb of sodium sulfide per lb mercury in the ore (1 to 4 moles sodium sulfide per mole mercury) and leaching in a 0.34-lb sodium cyanide per ton solution mixture. Gold-to-mercury ratios in solution increased from 43, with the use of 0.38 lb of sodium sulfide, to 141 with 1.5 lb of sodium sulfide. However, during ore leaching with a solution containing 6 lb sodium cyanide per ton of solution, sodium sulfide is not very effective in suppressing mercury extraction. The gold-to-mercury ratio in the solution increased from 0.95, without sulfide additions, to 12 when 0.78 lb of sulfide was used. When 2.5 lb of sodium sulfide was used for each pound of mercury in the ore, the ratio decreased to 4.5.

Table No. 4

EFFECT OF SODIUM CYANIDE AND SODIUM SULFIDE ON

GOLD, SILVER, AND MERCURY EXTRACTION

Sodium cyanide in leach solution, lb per ton	Sodium sulfide added, lb per lb Mercury (mole/mole mercury)	Percent Extraction Gold	Silver	Mercury	Ratio Gold to Mercury in Solution
0.34	0.38 (1/1)	98	11.4	0.37	43
0.34	0.75 (2/1)	94	13.3	0.17	122
0.34	1.50 (4/1)	94	11.4	0.14	141
6.0	0	89	16.0	19.4	1
6.0	0.19 (.5/1)	88	16.0	2.0	9
6.0	0.78 (2/1)	88	16.0	1.5	12
6.0	2.5 (6.5/1)	89	14.0	4.0	4

Two test series determined the effect of time after adding sulfide to a solution containing 0.34 lb and 1.0 lb sodium cyanide per ton of solution. Data in Table No. 5 show all the mercury is precipitated from the solution containing 0.34 lb sodium cyanide per ton in 15 min using 0.63 lb sodium sulfide per lb of mercury. However, almost 1% of the mercury is redissolved with 1/2 hr, and 3.6% is redissolved in 4 hr. With 1.0 lb of sodium cyanide per ton of solution, mercury extraction decreases to 3.4% 1/2 hr after adding sulfide, then increases to 15% in 2 hr.

Table No. 5

EFFECT OF SODIUM CYANIDE, SODIUM SULFIDE,

AND TIME ON GOLD AND MERCURY EXTRACTIONS

Sodium cyanide concentration, lb per ton	Sodium sulfide concentration, lb/lb mercury (mole/mole mercury)	Time after sulfide addition, hr	Extraction, percent		gold to mercury ratio in solution
			gold	silver	
0.34	0.63 (1.6)	0.25	94	<0.1	>400
		0.50	95	0.9	22
		1.00	95	1.6	13
		2.00	94	2.3	9
		3.00	97	3.0	7
		4.00	97	3.6	6
1.00	1.25 (3.2)	0.25	96	5.3	4
		0.50	92	3.4	6
		1.00	92	3.4	6
		1.50	93	12.6	2
		2.00	90	15.0	2

The tests reported in Tables No. 4 and 5 show the most effective suppression of mercury extraction in solutions containing low concentrations of sodium cyanide (0.34 lb per ton of solution) would require 2 to 4 moles (0.8 to 1.5 lb per lb of mercury) of sulfide per mole of mercury in the ore, and that a combination of strong sodium cyanide (above 1 lb per ton of solution) and sodium sulfide (1 lb per lb mercury) will cause rapid dissolution of the precipitated mercury sulfide. Mercury sulfide dissolution rates are variable, depending on leaching conditions.

Suppression of Mercury Extraction With Calcium Sulfide. Standard bottle leach tests were conducted to determine the effect of time after adding calcium sulfide on selective gold and silver separation from mercury. Five-hundred grams of ore were leached in 750 ml of solution containing 0.34 lb sodium cyanide per ton solution (0.17 gram sodium cyanide per liter) and 2.5 lb calcium oxide per ton ore. At the end of a 24-hr leach, calcium sulfide was added and solution samples were assayed periodically for gold, silver, and mercury. Table No. 6 and Figure III

Table No. 6

SELECTIVE EXTRACTION OF GOLD USING CALCIUM SULFIDE

Calcium sulfide lb/lb mercury* (mole/mole mercury)	Time after sulfide addition, hr	Extraction, percent**			gold:mercury ratio in solution
		gold	silver	mercury	
0.54 (1.5)	0	97.3	17.2	11.30	2
	0.25	99.5	17.2	3.40	6
	0.50	97.7	17.2	0.19	108
	2.00	98.2	17.2	0.19	108
	3.00	99.5	17.2	0.35	59
	4.00	100.0	17.2	0.42	49
	6.00	99.5	17.2	0.83	25
	7.00	100.0	17.2	0.75	28
0.18 (0.5)	0	92.3	22.3	9.40	2
	0.25	92.3	24.0	5.80	3
	1.00	96.8	25.7	2.10	10
	2.00	95.0	22.3	1.70	12
	3.00	96.4	24.0	2.00	10
	4.00	100.0	24.0	2.50	8
	7.00	91.9	22.3	4.00	5
	24.00	91.9	22.3	10.10	2

*Lb or mole mercury in the ore.
**Percent is based on solution and residue assay averages.

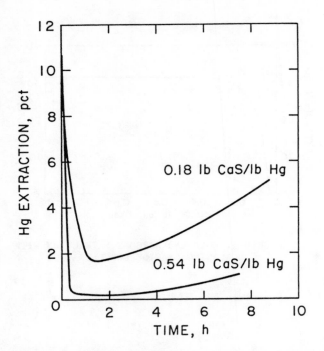

FIGURE III. EFFECT OF TIME ON SULFIDE PRECIPITATED MERCURY

show mercury extraction decreased from 11% before adding sulfide to 0.2% 1/2 hr after adding 0.54 lb calcium sulfide per lb of mercury (1.5 moles calcium sulfide per mole mercury). Three hours after adding sulfide, mercury started to slowly redissolve and reached 0.8% in 7 hr. When adding 0.18 lb calcium sulfide per lb mercury (1/2 mole calcium sulfide per mole mercury), extracted mercury gradually decreased from 9% before adding sulfide to 2% 1 hr after adding sulfide; after 3 hr it began increasing and reached 4% 7 hr after adding sulfide, and 10% 24 hr after adding sulfide. A separate test was completed using 100 grams of ore and 150 ml solution containing 0.34 lb sodium cyanide per ton and 2.5 lb calcium oxide per ton of ore. After leaching 24 hr, 2.88 lb calcium sulfide per lb mercury (8 moles calcium sulfide per mole mercury) were added, the slurry was rolled 1/4 hr, and the filtered solution was assayed. Gold-to-mercury ratios in solution were greater than 400 to 1. The solution assayed 0.0582 oz of gold and less than 0.00015 oz of mercury per ton. Gold and silver extractions were not affected by the calcium sulfide additions. These tests show calcium sulfide will effectively suppress mercury extraction and that the mercury does not begin to redissolve until after about 4 hr. Suppression of the mercury extraction is not as rapid with calcium sulfide as with sodium sulfide (compare Tables No. 5 and 7). However, redissolution of the precipitated mercury is more

Table No. 7

CARBON-IN-PULP SELECTIVE EXTRACTION OF GOLD AND SILVER

Ratio of CaS to Hg in ore, mole (lb)	Sample	Radioisotope counts			Ratio of counts on carbon to head slurry			Adsorption on carbon, percent			Calculated ratio gold:mercury
		gold	silver	mercury	gold	silver	mercury	gold	silver	mercury	
No sulfide added	Head slurry	3,130	3,226	7,065	NA*	NA	NA	NA	NA	NA	1
2/1 (.72)	Carbon stage 1	70,549	71,025	7,497	22.5	22.0	1.06	99.1	96.9	4.7	32
2/1 (.72)	Carbon stage 2	540	2,693	650	0.2	0.8	0.09	0.9	3.5	0.4	3
2/1 (.72)	Carbon stage 3	-4	268	504	0	0.1	0.07	0	0.4	0.3	0
Total on carbon		71,089	73,986	8,651	22.7	22.9	1.22	100.0	100.8	5.4	28
No sulfide added	Head slurry	2,636	2,499	5,139	NA*	NA	NA	NA	NA	NA	1
4/1 (1.44)	Carbon stage 1	55,645	50,985	400	21.11	20.40	0.08	99.4	96.0	0.4	228
4/1 (1.44)	Carbon stage 2	328	2,182	339	0.12	0.87	0.07	0.6	4.1	0.3	2
4/1 (1.44)	Carbon stage 3	32	290	215	0.01	0.12	0.04	0.06	0.6	0.2	0.3
Total on carbon		56,005	53,457	950	21.24	21.39	0.19	100.00	100.70	0.9	102

*NA = Not applicable since no carbon is present.

rapid with sodium sulfide than with calcium sulfide. Treating ore with calcium sulfide to suppress mercury extraction allows more time than sodium sulfide to separate dissolved gold and silver from the slurry by carbon adsorption before mercury begins to dissolve. Therefore, all subsequent tests were done using calcium sulfide.

Selective Extraction of Gold and Silver In a Simulated Carbon-In-Pulp Circuit. To determine selective extraction of gold and silver in a simulated CIP circuit, ground ore, lime (2.5 lb per ton), and cyanide solution (0.34 lb sodium cyanide per ton solution) were roll-leached in a plastic bottle to dissolve precious metals. After a 24-hr leach, the solution and residue were assayed for gold, silver and mercury. Calcium sulfide was added to slurry portions, and the mixture was rolled 1 hr and then contacted with 20 gram per liter of 6 x 16 mesh-activated carbon and rolled an additional hour. The carbon was advanced countercurrently to a new portion of slurry. To simulate a three-stage CIP circuit, the slurry was advanced to a second, and then a third bottle containing carbon. The total CIP circuit time was 4 hr after adding the calcium sulfide.

Analyses and distribution of precious metals were accomplished with radioisotopes of gold, silver, and mercury. Radioisotopes were added to the slurry following the 24-hr leach prior to addition of sulfide. Slurry samples were counted on the Gamma counter before and after adding carbon. Carbon from each stage was washed free of slurry and counted. Radioisotope counts on the head and tail slurries showed nearly 100% gold adsorption on the carbon; therefore gold adsorption was used as a standard for determining the percent adsorption of mercury and silver.

The percent mercury and silver on carbon is determined from the mathematical equation:

$$\text{Pct Hg} = 100 \times \frac{\text{Hg* cps on C/Hg* cps on head slurry}}{\text{Au cps on C/Au cps on head slurry}}$$

*Percent silver is determined by substituting silver counts for mercury counts.

Tests were conducted using 0.72 lb (2 moles) and 1.44 lb (4 moles) calcium sulfide per lb mercury in the ore.

Results of the sulfide rejection of mercury in the CIP circuit given in Table No. 7, show 95% of solubilized mercury is rejected utilizing 0.72 lb calcium sulfide per lb of mercury in the ore and 99% is rejected using 1.4 lb of calcium sulfide. The average gold to mercury ratio on the carbon was 28:1 with 0.72 lb calcium sulfide per lb mercury and 100:1 with 1.4 lb calcium sulfide per lb mercury, 4 hr after adding sulfide to the slurry. It is expected that an adsorption circuit requiring 4 hr or more to recover gold from solution would need more than 1.4 lb calcium sulfide per lb of mercury in the ore to obtain the best separation of mercury from precious metals. Each plant circuit would need to be tested to determine the optimum amount of sulfide to add.

Selective Extraction of Gold and Silver in a Simulated Grinding Circuit. Several commercial gold cyanide mill operations add cyanide directly to the ball mill to extract gold and silver during grinding. Over 80% of the gold and a portion of the mercury are solubilized at this time. Therefore, tests were completed to see whether calcium sulfide additions to the ball mill would depress mercury extraction without affecting gold extraction. Variations in calcium sulfide additions were from 0.36 to 2.88 lb per lb of mercury in the ore (1-8 chemical equivalent calcium sulfide per equivalent of mercury). One thousand grams of minus 10-mesh ore, 1.25 grams of calcium oxide (2.5 lb calcium oxide per ton of ore), 0.8 grams of sodium cyanide (0.53 lb per ton of solution), 1,000 ml of water, and calcium sulfide were added to the ball mill and ground 45 min with 10 kg of steel balls. The resulting slurry was washed into a 9-liter bottle with 2,000 ml of water and mixed. Slurry samples were taken for assay. Gold and silver were adsorbed from the slurry with 6 x 16 mesh activated carbon in three stages, over a 24-hr period. Carbon was removed from the slurry at the end of each stage and new carbon added. The first-stage carbon was in contact with the slurry for 4 hr, the second stage for 2 hr, and the third stage for 18 hr.

One gram of carbon (0.33 gram per liter) was utilized in each stage, instead of 20 grams per liter used in industry, so that the mercury loading would be high enough to measure. Gold, silver, and mercury on the carbon were assessed by neutron activation and counting on the Gamma counter. An additional test was conducted with 2.88 lb calcium sulfide per lb of mercury in the ore and without carbon in the slurry. The test without carbon produced 89% gold extraction by the end of the grinding period and 94% extraction after 4 hr. Forty-five minutes of grinding resulted in a 0.15% mercury extraction, which increased to 0.19% after 6 hr, and to 1.4% after 24 hr without carbon addition.

Carbon adsorption test results, shown in Table No. 8 and Figure IV, produced mercury recovery on the carbon of 5.5, 0.6, 0.4, and 0.2% with 0.36, 0.72, 1.44, and 2.88 lb calcium sulfide per lb of mercury in the ore, respectively; when on adsorption for 24 hr. Eighty-seven to ninety-one percent of the gold in the ore was recovered on 0.33 grams carbon per liter, while about 6% remained dissolved in the solution at the end of the tests. Dissolved gold recovery on the carbon is generally complete in about 4 hr, as reported in Table No. 7 and present industrial practice using 20 grams of carbon per liter of slurry.

Mercury adsorption on the carbon was 0.2% in 24 hr using 2.88 lb calcium sulfide per lb of mercury. More than 0.2% in a 6 hr adsorption time, using 20 grams of carbon per liter of slurry, would not be expected because this is the total amount dissolved in 6 hr without carbon.

Table No. 8

DISTRIBUTION OF GOLD, SILVER, AND MERCURY WHEN ADDING CALCIUM SULFIDE TO THE

BALL MILL, FOLLOWED BY A THREE-STAGE CIP

Calcium sulfide lb/lb mercury	End solution and solution samples			On carbon			Total extracted from ore			Metals in residue, percent		
	gold	silver	mercury	gold	silver	mercury	gold	silver	mercury	gold	silver	mercury
0.36	7.46	14.95	8.5	90.8	71.0	5.5	98.3	85.9	14.0	1.75	14.1	86.0
0.72	6.6	24.2	0.85	87.0	74.3	0.55	93.6	98.5	1.4	6.3	7.5	98.4
1.44	5.6	31.2	1.6	87.9	66.9	0.39	93.5	98.1	2.0	6.4	1.9	98.0
2.88	5.5	34.0	0.27	88.8	63.9	0.17	94.3	99.9	0.44	5.7	2.1	99.6

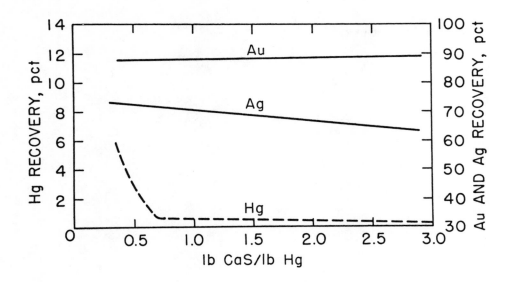

FIGURE IV. GOLD, SILVER AND MERCURY LOADING ON
CARBON, WITH INCREASING AMOUNTS OF CALCIUM SULFIDE

CONCLUSION

Calcium or sodium sulfides are effective in
suppressing extraction of mercury without
affecting gold or silver extraction in cyanide
solutions. Nearly 100% of the mercury is
rejected in the tailings with these sulfides.
Calcium sulfide is preferred because less than 1%
of the mercury was extracted from an ore in 7 hr
using 0.54 lb calcium sulfide per lb mercury in
the ore while 3.6% of mercury extraction was
attained in 4 hr with 0.63 lb of sodium sulfide.

Addition of calcium sulfide to a leach slurry,
prior to a simulated CIP circuit, resulted in
less than 1% of the mercury being adsorbed on the
carbon, while gold or silver recovery was
unaffected. Addition of sodium cyanide, lime,
and calcium sulfide to a simulated grinding
circuit, followed by a simulated CIP adsorption
circuit, recovered less than 0.2% of the mercury
on the carbon in a 24-hr adsorption time. Gold
and silver extractions from the ore were not
affected. Adsorption of dissolved silver from
the solution was low due to the low carbon
concentration in the slurry (0.3 grams per liter).
Mercury rejection in present mill operations would
require little modification to the mill flowsheet
so that mercury recovery on the carbon would be
less than about 0.2%.

REFERENCES

Clennell, J. E., 1915, The Cyanide Handbook,
McGraw-Hill, Inc., NY, pp. 16, 357.

Door, John V. N., and Bosqui, Francis L., 1950,
Cyanidation and Concentration of Gold and Silver
Ores, McGraw-Hill, Inc., NY, pp 238-246.

Flynn, C.M., Jr.,et al, 1981, "Selective Removal
of Mercury From Cyanide Solutions," U. S. Pat.
4,256,707, March 17, 1981.

Laxen, P.A., et al, 1979, "Developments in the
Application of Carbon-in-Pulp to the Recovery of
Gold From South African Ores," Journal of South
Africa Institute of Mining and Metallurgy, Vol.
79, No. 11, pp. 315-326.

Potter, G. M., and Bhappu, R. B., 1978, "The
Chemistry of Gold and Silver Recovery From
Natural Resources," American Chemical Society
Annual Meeting, Anaheim, Calif, March 1978.

Thorndycraft, R. Bruce, 1982, "Pinson Mining Company
Mill Design," 111th AIME Annual Meeting, Dallas,
Texas, February 14-18, 1982 (copy obtainable from
Bureau of Mines, Salt Lake City Research Center,
Salt Lake City, Utah.)

Chapter 13

CARBON ADSORPTION OF GOLD
MAXIMUM LOADING AND IONIC CONTAMINANT EFFECT
ON LOADING RATES

W.R. Boehme
Mountain States Research and Development
Tucson, Arizona 85731

George M. Potter
40 South Calcite Avenue
Tucson, Arizona 85745

ABSTRACT

The laboratory test work compares various 6 x 16 mesh activated coconut carbons using a gold standard solution of 4 ppm dissolved in sodium cyanide. The carbon adsorption rate and maximum loading are measured for different feed solution ionic contaminates: silver, copper, thiocyanate, and ferrocyanide.

Conclusions are drawn that among the activated coconut carbons tested, maximum loading and the effects of specific ions varied significantly. The work presented can be applied to 6 x 16 mesh carbon selection tests and specific ion monitoring for industrial carbon adsorption systems.

Introduction

The increased usage of activated carbon in the recovery of precious metals from leach solutions has been well recognized. The specific application of carbon adsorption to more complex gold and silver ores warrants the investigation into the effect of metallic ion interaction with gold adsorption.

The purpose of this research project was to quantify the individual effect on the loading of gold on carbon by some of the common ionic contaminants contained in industrial cyanide pregnant leach solutions. The method used was measurement of the rate of loading of gold from a feed solution containing 4 ppm gold in cyanide solution with individually spiked levels of a single contaminant.

The test work was done in two parts. In Part I, five 6 x 16 mesh activated coconut shell carbon samples made by four different manufacturers were evaluated as to their gold loading rate and total gold loading. The five carbon samples tested are not identified by manufacturer and are simply designated as Types "A" through "E". Then from the carbons tested, a suitable highly active carbon was selected for subsequent studies on impurity effects upon loading, Part II.

Test Procedures

The procedures and test descriptions are given for the maximum gold carbon loading tests and the dynamic gold carbon loading tests.

Maximum Loading Test

The method used for loading the 6 x 16 mesh coconut shell carbons was in accordance with the procedure developed at the U.S. Bureau of Mines Salt Lake laboratory. The testing apparatus is shown in Figure 1.

A 4.5 ppm gold solution was prepared by dissolving fine (-200 mesh) gold powder in a sodium cyanide solution made with deionized water at pH 10.5 (lime adjusted). This gold feed solution was fed by a metering pump at a rate of 2.5 ml/min. to each carbon loading column. The feed solution was analyzed for gold, silver and copper to monitor potential interference to gold loading.

The barren solutions were collected and the volume measured three times each day. The solutions were weighed, analyzed, and the pH determined. The solution feed rate was monitored daily.

The test duration was eleven days. All six columns were run simultaneously.

Dynamic Loading Test

The method used for determining the rate of gold loading onto carbon was from Fleming and Nicol (1983).(1)

A gold/cyanide solution was prepared in the same manner as previously stated. The solutions containing ionic contaminant were prepared in deionized water with appropriate amounts of sodium cyanide to dissolve powders of silver, copper, etc. The gold/cyanide solution was then mixed with the contaminant solution.

For each test, 6,000 grams of solution was contacted with 4 grams of activated 6 x 16 mesh coconut shell carbon. All carbon was from the same manufacturer and the same batch number.

Although for our dynamic loading test purposes carbon Type "E" was selected as the best, this might not be the case for another application. The various carbons tested for maximum loading had surface areas from 1200 m^2/g (Type "A" and "E") to 700 m^2/g (Type "B", "C", and "D"). Pore volume for type "A" and "E" carbons was 0.70 to 0.79 H_2O milliliters per gram while Type "B", "C", and "D" pore volume was not given.

Caution should be used in placing too much importance on high surface area and pore volume. These criteria by themselves are not adequate to define a highly activated carbon.

Carbon loading took place in 19 liter open end vessels on a set of rolls turning at 11 rpm. The solution pH was monitored periodically and solution aliquots of 20 milliliters were taken after the first one-half hour and hourly thereafter for four to five hours. Time started with the addition of the carbon.

Generally, the carbon loading test was stopped after 24 hours. The loaded carbon was filtered from the solution.

The solution aliquots and final solution were analyzed for gold, silver and copper or other contaminants by atomic absorption. The loaded carbon was analyzed by digestion with acids and the resulting solution read on the A.A. The data log sheets for each test with conditions, analyses and metals balance are available upon request.

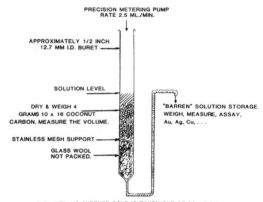

FIGURE 1 APPARATUS USED FOR MAXIMUM LOADING EXPERIMENT

PART I
Introduction—Maximum Loading Test

The research project was initiated through the suggestion and guidance of Mr. George Potter. The project was funded by Mountain States Mineral Enterprises.

The purpose of Part I of the research was to compare the rate and total gold loading of five commonly available 6 x 16 mesh activated coconut carbons under strictly controlled conditions. This permitted the selection of a highly active carbon for Part II impurity studies.

Activated coconut carbon prepared by various manufacturers is routinely used successfully by Mountain States Research and Development and by most carbon process gold operators to recover gold from leach solutions and slurries. However, comparative gold adsorption evaluation tests were performed to assure the selection for impurity-effect studies of an active carbon typical of the highly gold adsorptive carbon products now commerically available.

Discussion

The primary concern was to make all test conditions equal and hold all factors constant for each of five carbon columns.

The test conditions monitored and held constant were:
1. Feed rate of the gold solution.
    (2.5 milliliters per minute)
2. Feed solution gold content
    (4.5 ppm gold)
3. Feed solution pH
    (10.5)

Because the feed pumps were operated at the lowest end of their range, the feed rate to the columns was not as constant as desired. To eliminate the bias of feed rate variation the carbon loading of gold was graphed against the gold adsorption rate. These graphs are shown in Figures 2 through 5. The graphs show the level of feed rate variation was not a significant factor in adsorption rate or maximum loading.

The average feed rate and standard deviation of the average are shown for each carbon tested in Table I. Also shown in Table I is a comparison between the calculated ounces of gold adsorbed per ton of carbon at the end of the test and the fire assay of the final loaded carbon. The analytical comparison checks the data for carbon loading.

Table I Summary of Carbons

Carbon Type	A	B	C	D	E
Average Feed Rate	2.36	2.15	2.40	2.49	2.59
Standard Deviation	0.32	0.29	0.27	0.42	0.42
Maximum Loading (oz/ton Au)	1,006	356	260	275	839
Carbon Fire Assay	1,091	372	269	324	967
% Feed Gold Adsorbed On Last Test Day	50%	18%	12%	12%	29%

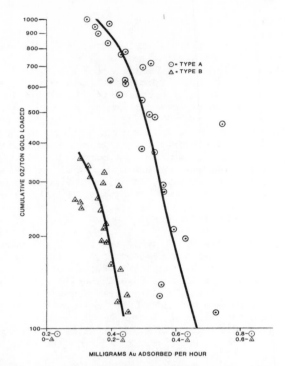

FIGURE 2 LOADING VERSUS ADSORPTION RATE FOR TYPE "A" AND "B" COCONUT SHELL CARBONS

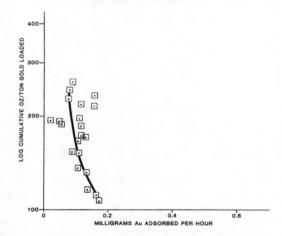

FIGURE 3 LOADING VERSUS ADSORPTION RATE FOR TYPE "C" COCONUT SHELL CARBON

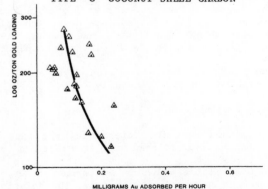

FIGURE 4 LOADING VERSUS ADSORPTION RATE FOR TYPE "D" COCONUT SHELL CARBON

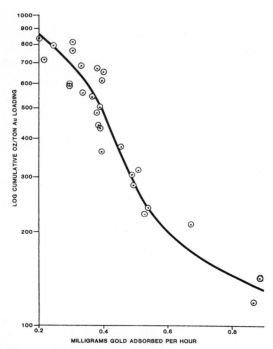

FIGURE 5 LOADING VERSUS ADSORPTION RATE FOR TYPE "E" COCONUT SHELL CARBON

Conclusion

The test work on side by side gold loading comparison of different manufacturers' carbons has shown two carbons, Type "A" and "E", are far superior in total loading and the rate of gold adsorption. The assumption that all 6 x 16 mesh coconut carbon performs equally is not valid and Type "E" carbon was selected for subsequent Part II solution impurity-effect tests.

Type "A" carbon had slightly better loading characteristics than Type "E" (Table I) but was not selected because of its brittle nature. A simple screening of the Type "A" and "E" carbons showed that "A" did not hold up as well as "E" to attrition. Also Type "E" carbon exhibited higher gold adsorbed per hour values than Type "A" carbon at loadings under 200 oz/ton. Compare figures 2 and 5.

PART II
Carbon Loading Dynamics

Pilot and commercial plant experience in the operation of carbon column and CIP gold adsorption processes suggests that various factors inhibit the gold adsorption rate and practical loadings in the carbon.

Previous work by C. A. Fleming and M. J. Nicol (1) indicates that ionic strength, the solution pH, solution temperature, absorbance of copper cyanides (under certain circumstances) and high concentrations of residual cyanides may notably affect the loading equilibrium. Organic compounds may also "poison" the carbon and cause lower loadings.

The main objective of this study was to determine the effect of silver, copper, ferrocyanide, and thiocyanate on the rate of gold loading on to coconut shell carbon. Comparisons were made between gold loading rates with and without the ionic contaminants.

Mechanism of Gold Adsorption

A brief description of the possible explanations for the adsorption of gold by activated carbon is given. A short discussion on loading mechanisms can aid in the understanding that ionic interactions are a significant factor in the dynamics of gold loading.

The gold dissolution by cyanide represented by the following chemical reaction, Finkelstein (1972) (2) and Hedley and Tabachnik (1968) (3):

$$2\ Au + 4\ CN^- + O_2 + 2\ H_2O \longrightarrow$$

$$2\ Au\,(CN)_2^- + 2\ OH^- + H_2O_2$$

The gold-cyanide complex that is formed by leaching is readily adsorbed by activated coconut shell carbon. The removal of the gold by the carbon is a diffusion controlled process. The diffusion rate for gold onto carbon is defined by Fick's law:

$$\frac{d\,(Au)}{dt} = \frac{D}{S}\,A([Au] - [Au]i)$$

where:

$\dfrac{d\,(Au)}{dt}$ = the rate of gold diffusion

D = the diffusion coefficient of gold complex

$[Au]$ = the gold complex activity in the bulk solution

$[Au]i$ = the gold cyanide complex activity at the carbon interface

A = the surface area upon which the adsorption takes place

S = the thickness of the boundary layer

The overall mass transfer of the gold-cyanide complex from the bulk solution requires at least two stages. One stage is the gold transfer from the bulk solution to the carbon surface. The second stage is the permeation of the gold complex from the surface to the interior adsorption sites. Most likely the outer surface of the carbon becomes saturated first (4). However the internal diffusion step has an effect on the rate process. The combination of boundary layer, surface, and internal diffusions should be considered.

Three adsorption theory mechanisms are listed:
1. Physical process due to Van der Waals forces.
2. Chemical complexes
3. Electrochemical

A reasonable explanation for the adsorption

of the gold-cyanide complex using the electro-chemical theory is given. In the presence of oxygen an aqueous activated carbon suspension will hydrolyze to form hydroxyl groups and H_2O_2. The carbon acquires a positive charge by supplying electrons to the hydrolysis. The positively charged carbon will attract the nega-tive $Au(CN_2)^-$ complex. The following reac-tion should take place (5):

$$O_2 + 2H_2O + 2e^- \longrightarrow H_2O_2 + 2OH^-$$

However, the electrochemical theory does not explain why $Hg(CN)_2$, a neutral complex, can compete with the $Au(CN)_2^-$ (6). For an explanation of the cluster-type compound gold adsorption mechanism, see Reference 6.

Specific Ion Effect on Rate of Loading

The individual ion effects on gold loading were measured at several different ionic concen-trations. First the loading rate from a 4 ppm gold solution in deionized water was determined. The following variables were held as near con-stant as possible for each test: solution volume, weight of carbon, temperature, starting solution feed ionic concentration, and agitation rate. All water used to make solutions was deionized before specific ion addition. The measured effects on gold loading for each con-taminant are summarized.

No Contaminant

The carbon loading rate and level for a gold only solution were determined for comparison to the contaminating ion tests. The loading rate for a 4 ppm gold solution with no contaminants was defined by the following equation.

    Log y = −0.16 x + (0.602)
    where:
y = ppm gold in deionized water
x = adsorption time in hours

The slope of the loading rate equation becomes more negative with an increase in the starting gold solution concentration. For a 4.8 ppm gold solution the slope was −0.21, Figure 6.

The carbon loading level for the 4 ppm gold solution was 150 oz/ton. A total of 4 grams of activated 6 x 16 mesh coconut shell carbon was contacted with 6,000 grams of the 4 ppm gold solution. The level of 150 oz/ton gold in the carbon accounts for 92% of the total gold in the feed solution after adjusting for solution aliquots and the final barren solution concen-tration.

Figure 6 illustrates the relationship of gold concentration in the solution versus the adsorp-tion time for loading the carbon. The graph in Figure 6, will be used for comparison to similar graphs with the specific ionic contaminants.

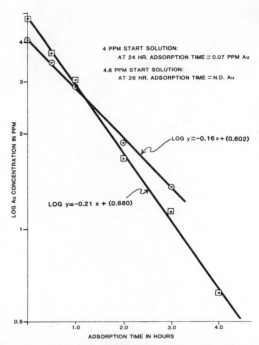

FIGURE 6   LOG GOLD CONCENTRATION VERSUS ADSORP-TION RATE FOR NO CONTAMINANT

Copper

Two carbon loading tests with copper dis-solved by using sodium cyanide solution were conducted at different copper concentrations. The test results are shown in Table II.

Table II Copper Contaminant

Test No.	Adsorption Time	Solution Concentration in ppm		
		Au	Cu	Free CN⁻
RB-24	0.0	3.77	204	28.4
"	0.5	3.22	183	—
"	1.1	2.88	182	—
"	2.0	2.71	180	—
"	3.0	2.50	187	18.4
"	24.0	1.51	173	—
RB-28	0.0	4.66	108	145.0
"	0.6	3.36	108	—
"	1.4	2.47	107	—
"	2.0	1.68	106	—
"	3.2	1.06	107	—
"	4.0	0.79	106	—
"	20.0	0.10	105	—
"	24.0	0.10	107	—
"	28.0	0.10	102	—
"	46.0	0.10	105	67.9

Figure 7 shows the effect of the Copper Cyanide ion on the gold loading. At a 200 ppm Cu concentration in the gold solution the gold loading rate was drastically decreased while the effect of gold loading at 100 ppm Cu was mini-mal. Copper cyanide ions were shown to reduce gold loading at 200 ppm Cu concentration.

An explanation for the effects of copper

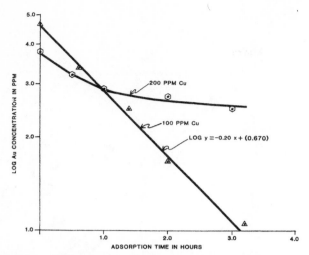

FIGURE 7 LOG GOLD CONCENTRATION VERSUS ADSORP-
TION TIME FOR COPPER AS A CONTAMINANT

loading onto carbon is given by Fleming and
Nicol (1). The free cyanide concentration plays
an important part in copper loading. The previous study by Fleming and Nicol showed that at
low ratios of free cyanide to copper, the copper
complex $Cu(CN)_2^-$ loads well onto carbon. At
high ratios of free cyanide to copper,
$Cu(CN)_2^{2-}$ and $Cu(CN)_4^{3-}$ species are
formed and do not load appreciably onto carbon.

The ratio of free cyanide to copper in solution for tests RB-24 and RB-28, Table II, showed
copper loading well at 1:5 ratio of free cyanide
to copper. However, at 3:2 and 2:3 free cyanide
to copper ratios the copper did not appreciably
load. Thus, to lessen the loading of copper,
the ratio of free cyanide to copper should be
monitored and kept high enough to assure the
$Cu(CN)_2^-$ complex is not present.

A chemical analysis of the loaded carbon for
the 200 ppm Cu test revealed a 4% copper content
and 99 oz/ton gold. The gold contained in the
carbon represented 60.7% of the original gold in
the starting feed solution. The remaining gold
stayed in solution without being adsorbed. The
copper adsorbed by the carbon was 14.7% of the
original feed. The gold metallurgical balance
gave 106% of the starting feed and the copper
balance showed 97% of the starting feed.

Silver

Silver was dissolved in a sodium cyanide
solution. Silver concentrations of 10 and 4.5
ppm were tested on carbon loading gold solutions
containing 4.5 - 4.6 ppm Au. The test results
are given in Table III.

The graph in Figure 8 demonstrates the adverse effect of silver as a contaminant for the
loading of gold. Silver and gold in the ratio
of approximately 1:1 were shown to decrease the
gold loading rate and probably the ultimate
loading of gold onto carbon. Silver in solution
with gold at approximately 2:1 ratio (10.6 ppm
Ag: 4.6 ppm Au) has a pronounced effect on
decreasing gold adsorption.

The analysis of the loaded carbon for test

RB-25 disclosed a 129 oz/ton gold content with
63.8% of the original gold contained in the
carbon. The calculated silver content in the
loaded carbon was 175 oz/ton. The metals
balance gave a 103% accounting of the gold and a
large over accounting of silver, 199%. (The
loaded carbon silver assay was assumed to be in
error).

Table III Silver Contaminant

Test No.	Adsorption Time	Solution Concentration in ppm		
		Au	Ag	Free CN⁻
RB-25	0	4.59	10.63	458
"	0.5	3.87	9.94	-
"	1.0	3.39	9.77	-
"	2.0	2.85	9.60	-
"	3.0	2.61	9.39	-
"	4.0	2.40	9.29	445
"	24.0	1.68	9.29	384
RB-29	0	4.49	4.97	393
"	0.7	3.36	4.01	-
"	1.4	2.57	3.53	-
"	2.0	1.99	3.15	-
"	3.2	1.41	2.78	-
"	4.0	1.10	2.54	-
"	20.0	0.24	1.68	-
"	24.0	0.21	1.65	-
"	28.0	0.24	1.71	-
"	47.0	0.17	1.51	254

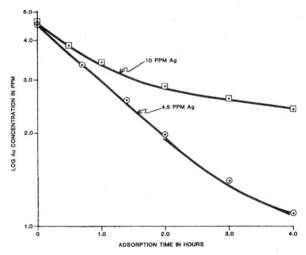

FIGURE 8 LOG GOLD CONCENTRATION VERSUS ADSORP-
TION TIME FOR SILVER AS A CONTAMINANT

Iron (Ferrocyanide)

Iron contaminant levels of approximately
2,000 and 1,000 ppm were tested for gold loading
rate with a 4 ppm gold solution. The iron contaminant was produced by dissolving sodium
ferrocyanide crystals in deionized water.

No effect on the gold loading rate was
observed with iron contaminant at the stated
levels. Figure 9 shows the almost identical
loading curves. A comparison between Figure 6
and Figure 9 demonstrates the similarity in
loading with no contaminant present. Also the

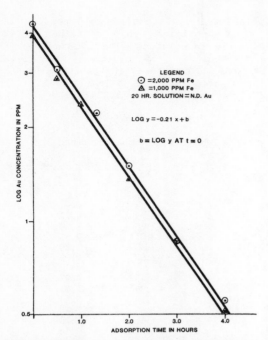

FIGURE 9 LOG GOLD CONCENTRATION VERSUS ADSORP-
TION RATE FOR IRON AS A CONTAMINANT

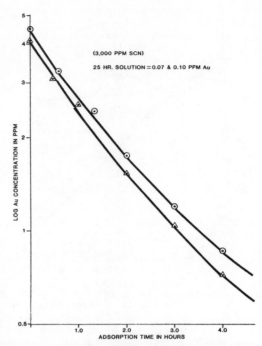

FIGURE 10 LOG GOLD CONCENTRATION VERSUS ADSORP-
TION RATE FOR THIOCYANATE AS A CON-
TAMINANT

slope of the lines are near identical for both the no contaminant and Fe contaminant graphs.

Ferrocyanide at the two stated levels did not affect the rate of loading. The carbons in the two tests loaded to 161 and 155 oz/ton gold. The gold balance indicated reasonable account-ability at 89% and 94% of the starting solution gold contents.

Thiocyanate

Solutions of 1,000 and 3,000 ppm thiocyanate were made by dissolving sodium thiocyanate crys-tals in deionized water and mixing the test solution with a 4 ppm gold solution.

The loading rate tests indicated thiocyanate is not as detrimental as copper or silver con-taminants. However, in comparison of thio-cyanate test results with no contaminant (gold only) loading rates, it was apparent that some decrease in loading rate occurred. At four hours of adsorption time the gold remaining in solution is 16% and 39% higher for the solutions containing 1,000 and 3,000 ppm thiocyanate com-pared to the no contaminate loading at four hours.

Figure 10 illustrates the very gradual decrease in gold loading rate with adsorption time.

The gold metals balance was only fair at 86% and 82% of the original feed accounted for in the final products.

The carbons in the two tests loaded to 143 and 153 oz/ton gold.

High CN⁻

Two solutions were prepared by dissolving reagent grade sodium cyanide granules in deio-nized water to make 2,400 and 11,000 ppm CN^- concentrations.

The test data points are given graphically in Figure 11. The final solution concentration after twenty-six hour adsorption time was 0.31 ppm Au and 0.48 ppm Au for the 2,400 and 11,000 ppm CN^- test solutions, respectively. This

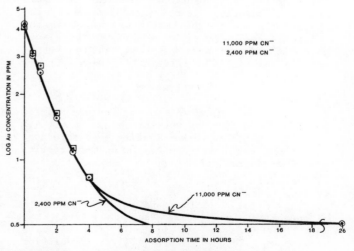

FIGURE 11 LOG GOLD CONCENTRATION VERSUS ADSORP-
TION RATE FOR HIGH FREE CYANIDE AS A
CONTAMINANT

represents gold carbon adsorption recoveries of 89.8% and 86%.

The high cyanide concentrations inhibited the loading rate. The analysis of the loaded carbon showed 144 and 131 oz/ton gold content. A total of 86% of the original gold feed was accounted for in both tests.

Conclusions/Summary

The laboratory testing has shown that it is important to carefully select the right activated carbon for the right application. A definition of the attributes that a specific carbon should have is the beginning for selection of the correct carbon.

The use of activated coconut shell carbon will continue to expand. More has been learned about the wider application of carbon to gold adsorption. The effects of ionic contaminants on gold loading onto carbon do require more study.

The future should indicate a wider range of gold carbon adsorption applications.

REFERENCES

1. Fleming, C. A. and Nicol, M. J., 1983, "The Adsorption of Gold onto Activated Carbon III. Factors Influencing the Rate of Loading and The Equilibrium Capacity", Paper to be submitted for publication in the Journal of South African Mining and Metallurgy.

2. Finkelstein, N. P., 1972, "The Chemistry of the Extraction of Gold from Its Ores", Gold Metallurgy in South Africa, ed. R.J. Adamson, Chamber of Mines of South Africa, Chapter 10, pp. 284-351.

3. Hedley, N. and Tabachnick, H., December 1968, Chemistry of Cyanidation, American Cyanamid Company, Mineral Dressing Notes, No. 23.

4. Smith, S. B., Hiltgen A.X., and Juhola, A.J. 1959, "Kinetics of Batch Adsorption of Dichlorophenol on Activated Carbon", Chemical Engineering Process Symposium, Vol. 55, No. 24, pp. 25 - 36.

5. Habashi, Fathi, unpublished manuscripts.

6. McDougall, G, J., Hancock, R. D., Nicol, M. J., Wellington, O. C., Copperthwaite, R. G., 1980, "The Mechanism of the Adsorption of Gold Cyanide on Activated Carbon", Journal of the South African Institute of Mining and Metallurgy, Vol. 80, No. 9, pp. 344 - 356.

Chapter 14

PANEL DISCUSSION

WATER CHEMISTRY OF HEAP LEACHING OPERATIONS

Robert S. Shoemaker
San Francisco Mining Associates
235 Montgomery Street
San Francisco, California 94104

Larry D. Hartzog
Bechtel Civil and Minerals, Inc.
50 Beale Street
San Francisco, California 94105

PANELISTS

Paul Chamberlin, Nerco Minerals
Jim Gourdie, Goldfield Mining Corp.
Roger Leonard, Cyprus Northumberland Mining Co.
Eric Daniels, Tenneco Minerals
John Dasher, Consulting Metallurgist
Bob Shoemaker, San Francisco Mining Associates
Larry Hartzog, Bechtel Civil and Minerals, Inc.

The Panelists

Mr. Paul Chamberlin.

Paul first started as a metallurgist for Anaconda, then was smelter metallurgist at Inspiration, a process engineer at Hazen Research, a senior metallurgist at Conoco Minerals, a staff metallurgist at Occidental Minerals, and is now Manager of Metallurgy for Nerco Minerals, the successor to Occidental, where he is responsible for monitoring all of their metallurgical operations, particularly Candelaria Partners and Alligator Ridge.

Mr. Jim Gourdie.

Jim received his Bachelor and Master degrees in Metallurgical Engineering from Michigan Tech. He was 12 years at Kennecott, where he became Mill Superintendent at the Chino Mines Division. In 1981 he went with Goldfield Mining Corporation on the Ortiz Project as Plant Superintendent and in July of 1983 he became Resident Manager at Ortiz.

Mr. Roger Leonard.

Roger has been a metallurgist with Utah International, Pioneer Nuclear, Pinson Mining Company, and Bateman Engineering, and he is presently, since November of 1982, Plant Superintendent at Cyprus Northumberland Mining Company, Austin, Nevada.

Mr. Eric Daniels.

Eric received his B.S. in Chemistry at Boise State University. Eric was an assayer at Delamar Silver, an assayer at Alligator Ridge, and then he was Chief Chemist and now Plant Supervisor at Tenneco Minerals Borealis Project, a 2500 ton/day heap-leach operation, near Hawthorne, Nevada.

Mr. John Dasher.

John has had a lengthy career as a hydrometallurgist. He worked with Bob Shoemaker at Bechtel for 15 years. According to Webster's Dictionary – Dasher: that which agitates or stirs things up.

Mr. R.S. Shoemaker.

Vice President
San Francisco Mining Associates

Mr. L.D. Hartzog.

Principal Engineer
Bechtel Civil & Minerals Inc.

The Operations

Candelaria

Mine	Open pit
Throughput	10,300 tpd
Agglomeration	Cyanide solution
Pregnant Solution Flow	2400 gpm
Recovery Circuit	Zinc precipitation
Crush Size	Minus 1 inch
Heap Height	60 ft

Alligator Ridge

Mine	Open pit
Throughput	3000 tpd
Agglomeration	Cyanide and lime
Pregnant Solution Flow	900 gpm
Recovery Circuit	Carbon adsorption
Crush Size	Minus 3/4 inch
Heap Height	40 ft

Ortiz

Mine	Open pit
Throughput	3500 tpd
Agglomeration	No
Pregnant Solution Flow	850 gpm
Recovery Circuit	Carbon adsorption
Crush Size	Minus 3/4 inch
Heap Height	23 ft

Northumberland

Mine	Open pit
Throughput	3000 tpd
Agglomeration	Cement
Pregnant Solution Flow	500 gpm
Recovery Circuit	Carbon adsorption
Crush Size	Minus 1/2 inch
Heap Height	20 ft

Borealis

Mine	Open pit
Throughput	2500 tpd
Agglomeration	Cement & cyanide
Pregnant Solution Flow	300-400 gpm
Recovery Circuit	Zinc precipitation
Crush Size	Minus 1 inch
Heap Height	12 ft

Shoemaker:

Every gold and silver plant today, whether it be heap leaching or other type of plant, has scaling problems. Most of these plants could not operate without anti-scaling reagents, or at least operations would be extremely difficult, particularly in heap leaching. Today we believe that we will all be able to learn something about these problems, and hopefully, the results of this session will be helpful to many of the people in attendance and the reader of the transcript of the session.

Dasher:

Good afternoon, ladies, gentlemen, and fellow-engineers. I appreciate this opportunity to speak to you. I did not come because I am expert in this subject, although I am more than 80 kilometers, that is fifty miles, from home. I came because the co-chairmen, with whom I have long been associated, knew I was 99% unemployed and would have plenty of time to prepare to speak.

Long ago, when I was transferred to the College Park, Maryland Station of our Bureau of Mines' Non-Metals Division, I was surprised to find that the major activity was a water treatment project, sponsored by the railroads, to learn about caustic embrittlement of the fire tube boilers of steam locomotives. I asked what this had to do with non-metallic minerals. The late Oliver Ralston explained that water was our most abundant non-metallic mineral. I had to agree. I recalled a story of a preacher who was overly concerned with the proper form of baptism. While preaching from the dry text of Genesis 1:1, "In the beginning God created the Heavens and the Earth," he began. And how did He create the Earth? One fourth land and three fourths water. What was all that water for? Baptism by immersion.

Water is certainly our most abundant mineral. It is also cheap.

In the East, process water can usually be pumped from a river to a height of, say 30 m (100 ft) at a cost of 0.1 ¢/Wd with power at 4 ¢/kWh or 1/2 ¢/t. That is very cheap. This is 1 000 gpm at $1/h. In the West, cheap water is also available for irrigation, with Government subsidy. Even for hydrometallurgy, water is dirt cheap. This does not apply to that which might be distilled from the local lake.

Sea water can be desalted by any of several distillation processes with an energy requirement of 230 kJ/1 (100 BTU/lb). With oil at 18 ¢/L or $29/bbl, the energy bill is $1/m^3 and $1/t or $3.80/1000 gal. Although energy may be only half the cost of this expensive form of water, it is comparable to delivered sand or gravel, or the cost of getting gold ore to the heaps, and, if required, the residue to a reclaimed emplacement.

Sea and brackish water can be purified by diffusion. This is the reverse osmosis process. It takes less energy than destillation, but it uses more costly electric energy.

Water can be fully demineralized by ion exchange, using both cationic and anionic resins. This costs less than distillation, when the mineral content is substantially less than that of the sea. For many purposes, softening is a quite satisfactory treatment. Soft water is that which does not leave a ring around the tub or the sink. Such rings are the insoluble soaps of calcium and magnesium.

The most common anion in fresh water is bicarbonate. It comes mainly from dissolving carbon dioxide from the air. Calcium and magnesium have soluble bicarbonates. When water is heated and/or treated with an alkali, bicarbonate becomes carbonate, and calcium and magnesium have insoluble carbonates, which then precipitate. Unfortunately, these precipitates like to form scale on surface, whether hot or cold.

Softening processes include hot and cold lime-soda processes, and the use of zeolites or cation exchange resins. All these cost less than desalting the sea. Boilers need soft water and so does froth flotation with fatty acids. Heap leaching normally does not.

Today we are concerned with heap leaching. Heap leaching costs less than agitation leaching, especially in capital. It is attractive when coarse crushing gives adequate access of solution to the mineral values. Heap leaching is used to recover oxide and sulfide copper, uranyl and uranous, native and sulfide silver, and gold from ores with or without carbon or other precipitants.

Leaching copper is done with acid plus ferric ions and with bacteria when sulfides are present. Uranium can be leached with acid or carbonate-bicarbonate solutions plus an oxidant if uranous values are present. I do not know if bugs help with uranium, but long ago I noted something like "mother of vinegar" in old samples of lab acid leach tests. Also uranium is recovered from copper dump leach liquors, when bugs make the reagents. When copper heap leaching is combined with cementation, iron accumulates in the solution and precipitates as hydrous ferric oxides and jarosite. When solvent extraction is used, this problem vanishes.

I have heard of no problems with fouling or scaling when uranium is leached with acid, in heaps or in situ. However, carbonate-bicarbonate leaching has scaling problems. Yesterday, Yan described the Mobil seed cone answer (83-311)

For heap leaching gold and/or silver, alkali-cyanide solutions are used, some oxygen is required, and for carbonaceous or sulfide ores more is needed. Cyanide is an appreciable expense, and to put it mildly, somewhat toxic. HCN is a volatile acid and much more volatile than acidic.

Leach solutions, therefore, need to be alkaline, and in alkaline solutions, as I have already mentioned, bicarbonate becomes carbonate, and calcium and magnesium carbonates precipitate, which can cause scaling. This occurs whether or not lime is used to make-up water supply and/or in the ore being leached. It is true that more calcium is present to cause scaling when lime is used as a source of the required alkalinity. It is also true that more carbonate ions are present when soda ash is used than when caustic soda is employed, and when heating the solution is done by submerged combustion. The problem can be minimized by using a more expensive alkali, but not eliminated.

When I was concerned with the flotation of non-metallic minerals in unsoftened water using fatty acids, some co-workers advocated adding some sodium hexametaphosphate, called "Calgon," to inhibit the precipitation of the collector by the water's hardness. Calgon was also said to avoid scaling in pipes, when used in substoichiometric quantities. It is still advocated to keep spots off of glassware in the dishwasher. That is a kind of scale. I could not imagine a hexavalent ion, and think I got better results with tetrasodium-pyrophosphate, which was also cheaper.

Organic phosphates have been met along the way as extractants of uranium, zinc, cobalt, and other metals from the aqueous to the organic phase.

There is also one supplied by N.L. Treating Chemicals (7077E Speedway, Suite 202, Tucson, AZ 85710) called Barochem S-35. It is an organic phosphonate scale inhibitor that has been used at Gold Acres (E and MJ, 7/77, p.67) at Borealis (panelist Daniels has the details) at Ortiz, per panelist Gourdie, at Candelaria, per panelist Chamberlin, and at some Southwest copper leach operations.

While uranium was a secret, I was working at MIT, and we were sent some domestic ores that contained montmorillonite. These leached but would not thicken or filter. The late Professor Gaudin came up with the idea of using some coarse form of resin in the pulp to absorb the uranium, and this led to several RIP plants. About this time Dow introduced Separan, a polyacrylate, which was a powerful flocculant. Other similar reagents soon appeared. With these, there were no more unthickenable, unfilterable pulps, and the need for RIP vanished.

Somehow, polyacrylates can also be scale inhibitors. Nalco (2801 Butterfield Rd, Oak Brook, 1L 60521) introduced one originally called 8830, now called 7811, which is a highly anionic dispersant, the opposite of Separan, and a scale inibitor which, unlike the flocculants, does not leave the solution to bind the slimes together.

It has been used at Ortiz, per Gourdie and at Alligator Ridge, per Chamberlin. Nalco also furnishes equipment to permit operators to receive bulk deliveries.

Drew Chemical (Drew Chemical Plaza, Boonton, NJ 07005) offers several Millsperse reagents containing a polymer called Isoquest LT. This is touted as being better than various polyacrylate and organic phosphorous reagents. I did not find this formula. Millsperse 802 is used in the copper plant that formerly used an organic phosphonate, at Candelaria, per Chamberlin, at a Northumberland, per Leonard, after other reagents had been tried.

Drew also has Millsperse 804 with the Isoquest polymer plus an organophosphorous compound, and Millsperse 806 with unnamed ingredients. Drew offers a side stream test unit called PULSE to measure scaling and fouling rates. Duke described it yesterday (83-327). It has a heated wall. One of the competitors says heated wall side stream tests do not help. I have no knowledge or opinion on this matter. I am not an expert. All suppliers claim that they analyze the situation to optimize dosage; technical help comes with the product. I understand why these methods are proprietary.

I do not understand why and how these reagents manage to prevent or greatly minimize scale. I do not know why scale forms on unheated surfaces, I think I understand boiler scale forming on a heated surface. As to what happens, the suppliers have furnished pictures. Fig. 1 from Nalco shows the rhomboids of calcite when no scale inhibitor is used. The 2000 X probably applies to the 5" x 6" original. Here it is at least 40,000 X. Fig. 2 shows the rounded lump resulting from the use of 7811. Fig. 3, from Drew, shows some needle clusters in the blank. That is also calcite. And Fig. 4, from Drew, some rounded clumps, after addition of Isoquest. To me, the blanks differ by more than the "after" pictures. I am glad the scale can be controlled. I do not need to know how these compounds work.

Lastly, I want to give you a case history I received from Tom De Mull of Amselco Alligator Ridge, who spoke yesterday even though it includes much that panelist Chamberlin could also tell you. Use of Nalco 7811 began in September, 1982, and operations were suspended during the winter. Other changes have been made. Improved heap preparation increased percolation rate; another type of sprinkler has proved to be more reliable; production has increased almost 50% above that of the previous period; about 1/4 of the improvement is attributed to the descalant. Its use costs $15 per operating hour. The average flow this year is 57 L/s (900 gpm) compared to 36.5 L/s (578 gpm) previously. Caustic is added to the hard makeup water entering the barren pond, the carbonates precipitated do not settle but scale the pump and pipes that return the solution with makeup chemicals to the leach heaps. The pump had to be descaled manually every two weeks and the pipes almost as often. With 7811 addition, neither has been descaled this year. The carbon formerly picked up 10% to 30% calcite each cycle. Since adding 7811 to the pregnant solution, it gets only 6% to 16% calcite in two to three cycles. Calcite is removed with nitric acid and much less is now required. Nozzles in the bottom of the carbon absorption tanks no longer need regular cleaning. Dosage is 12 mg/L to barren 20 mg/L to makeup water, and 30 mg/L to the pregnant.

Shoemaker:

Thank you very much, John. We appreciate your comments.

Question.

Briefly describe the scaling problems that you have encountered at your operation. What type of anti-scaling reagents you use and at what points in the circuits you add them?

Paul Chamberlin:

I'm going to comment about both Candelaria and Alligator Ridge. At Candelaria, when we first started operations, the worst scale that we noted was in the preg pumps, the preg lines and on filter cloths in both the clarifying filters and the precipitation presses. It should be noted that we did not add any anti-scaling agents at all for the first several months of operation. When we noticed scale problems occurring, we started adding one of the phosphanates and immediately curtailed the rather rapid accumulation of scale. However the scale continued to build up but at a much slower rate. The phosphonate seemed to soften the scale quite a bit. During that first year or so when we used the phosphonates, we had to pig the preg lines a couple of times. Later we had the circuit analyzed to find out where our major fouling problems were occurring. We determined that instead of adding anti-scaling agents in a number of places we could reduce the addition to two or three points. The scale is mostly calcium carbonate. We do not seem to have any calcium sulphate problems and we do not seem to have a lot of silica problems even though we are running a sodium system. When we started using a different anti-scaling agent, malaic anhydride, much of the scale disappeared. Now the scale problems are minimal. There is just a thin film of it in pipelines and in pumps, and continued use of the anti-scaling agent is keeping the scale under control.

At Alligator Ridge scaling has been almost entirely calcium carbonate with very little calcium sulphate and not much silica scale. The worst scaling has occurred in water makeup pumps, at the water treatment plant, at the preg pumps feeding the adsorption columns and at the barren pumps feeding the heaps. During the first year of operation, the scale slowly built up in the circuit. We did not add very much anti-scaling reagent and we did not have an acid washing circuit to take care of fouled carbon. When we

completed mining the first of three pits, Vantage One, and began mining the Vantage Two we encountered a more acidic ore. We changed from a sodium system to a lime system and we noticed a much greater amount of calcium carbonate scale build up in the circuit. About the same time, we had an acid wash circuit installed and began using a polyacrylate anti-scaling agent. Even though we had more scale in the circuit, the reagent kept the scale under control.

Jim Gourdie:

The Ortiz operation started up in February of 1980, and we started up without any water treatment chemicals. Carbonate fouling the carbon was very serious with loadings of 25%-30% calcium carbonate on carbon. We were not extracting gold very readily under those conditions. Ortiz began using a water treatment chemical, one of the polyphosphanates, and the calcium loading dropped to the 5% range. At the same time, we commissioned an acid wash facility and that came on stream in November of the following year. With acid washing we were able to reduce the 5% or 10% carbonate loading on carbon down to less than 1% before it was returned to the circuit. We subsequentaly changed water treatment chemicals and are now using a polyacrylate. In November of 1983, Ortiz installed a submerged combustion heater to heat barren solutions during the winter months, similar to the system used at Smoky Valley. We had done a lot of test work ahead of time and thought possibly we could control the scale that was going to form as the result of combustion gases in the barren solution. We upped our dosage to about 40 ppm before and after the heater and, to a degree, we were successful. We kept the scale from forming in the major pipelines and in the pumps. But in our sprinkler grid system the scale came out of solution and we fought through the winter keeping the sprinklers descaled. We are now in the process of installing a heat exchanger system so we can indirectly heat our barren solutions and we are looking forward to much better performance this winter.

Roger Leonard:

It's a lot easier to talk about scale at Northumberland now because we don't have a scaling problem. From startup through 1982, we had some terrible problems; spray availability was never any better than 90%. We had scale forming in the carbon columns and bridging the carbon and every five or six days we had to shut down the sprays and clean the scale out of the spray pump to keep it running. One of the first things tried at Northumberland was scrapping the milk of lime alkalinity control in favor of caustic soda. There was really no effect here.

We tried two brands of polyphosphonates and actually that aggravated the problem. We simply spread the scale throughout the spray lines and we had a dropping out of carbonate precipitates everywhere. To actually solve the problem, we had had to have a combination of mechanical changes,

changes in the plant operating conditions and a change in anti-scale reagents. I think the biggest change we made was upping the caustic addition. Right now we have to add about 0.6 pound per ton of caustic to solution sprayed and this is enough to drop out all of the carbonates in two ponds. We run a recirculating leach system with a barren pond and a low preg pond. We essentially soften the water from about 300 ppm calcium carbonate hardness to about 50 before we spray. We changed the PVC pipe to HDPE pipe. When we have scale problems, we can open up the pipe and pound on it a little bit, even in the winter time. We switched over to open impeller type spray pumps instead of closed impellers and we did not have so many problems with scale building-up. The biggest change, other than keeping the caustic high, was changing the anti-scale chemical. We tried both polyacrylate and malaic acid based reagents. Both of them worked well for the scale. Any scale that does form is slimy and can be wiped out. It is not a hard crystalline scale that has to be chiselled out of pipes. We did an evaluation checking flowmeter tubes for scale build-up to see which of the two products worked best and on a cost basis they work about the same. The dosage being within 2 or 3 ppm of each other. We opted to go to the malaic acid based reagent because we noticed some problems with carbon fouling using the polyacrylate. The only other change we really made was to keep our carbon bed fluidized at all time, so if we had any scale on it, it would not bridge the particles and block or channel the flow. We instituted acid washing 100% of the carbon after regeneration.

Eric Daniels:

At the Borealis Project we have been relatively fortunate in that our scaling problems are relatively minor. We have been using organic phosphanates since startup in October 1981. The scaling problems that we have observed have been limited to pump impellers on the preg, barren, and booster pumps. During the summer we usually add our chemical at the preg sump. However, we also utililize a submerged combustion heater and in the winter months it is necessary to increase our reagent additions at the barren sump and at the booster sump before the solution goes on to the pads. This is to keep the sprinkler lines free and clear.

Chamberlin:

At Candelaria, we add about 55 cc/min of reagent to 2500 gpm of solution, 15 cc's to the zinc cone, 20 cc's a minute to the barren as its exits from the precipitation presses, and about 20 cc's a minute to the preg sump. At Alligator Ridge, we add the polyacrylate at the rate of about 30 ppm to the preg solution, 12 ppm to the barren, and about 20 ppm to the fresh water makeup, and we also add about 200 ppm to the strip solution to avoid precipitation on the hot side of the heat exchanger.

Max El Tawil - ASARCO:

Does any of the the panelists have any experience with magnetic treatment of water for inhibition of scales, such as is being used in boiler feed water?

Gus Gustafson - NALCO:

In response to the question about the magnetic treatment of water, I believe this was tried at Cortez ten years ago at least, maybe fifteen. I understand it was a dismal failure. A supplier brought in the equipment for a no-cost trial for thirty days or so and they took it out because it was not effective.

Question -

What is the analysis of the fresh water you use? Carbonates, bicarbonates, calcium, sodium chloride, total hardness, and total dissolved solids.

Daniels:

All of these are in ppm: bicarbonate 129, calcium 34, sodium 35, chloride 13, total hardness 125 and the total dissolved solids is 321.

Leonard:

We get our water from a series of wells so I am going to give an average blend of our makeup water. It has pH 7.6 so there is no carbonate. Reported as ppm, bicarbonate 346, calcium 90, sodium 154, chloride 34, sulfite 281, total hardness 410, and total dissolved solids 952.

Gourdie:

At Ortiz, the alkalinity expressed as carbonates is around 300 milligrams per liter, bicarbonates 270, calcium 23, chloride 8, total hardness 485, total dissolved solids 322.

Chamberlin:

At Candelaria, bicarbonate 194 mg/L, calcium 36 mg/L, the sodium 54 mg/L, chloride 30 mg/L, hardness 170 mg/L, total dissolved solids 428 mg/L. At Alligator Ridge, bicarbonate 221 mg/L, calcium 56 mg/L, sodium 20 mg/L, total hardness is 248 mg/L.

Question -

Do you pretreat your fresh water? If so, how, and what is the analysis of the water after treatment?

Chamberlin:

At Candelaria we do not give the water any separate treatment. We add makeup water at about 400 gpm, as an annual average. It is added to the zinc slurry, with the sodium cyanide and to the barren pond. Undoubtedly we get some precipitation from all this makeup water but the anti-scaling reagents that are in the process streams effectively prevent the scale from giving any problems.

At Alligator Ridge the makeup water averages 300 gpm and it is treated separately, first by adding some zinc phosphate to the wells to inhibit corrosion in the casing (the well water itself is about 150 ppm in calcium, 100°F, 6.8 pH) and then by adding sodium hydroxide and polyacrylates in a separate water treatment facility. Makeup water is used to educt carbon throughout the system and for cooling water in the preg strip.

Gourdie:

Ortiz does not pretreat its fresh water. Our makeup water amounts to about 65 gpm, on an annualized average. Predominantly our makeup water is just to replace that lost to evaporation and the small amount that leaves with the residue. The bulk of makeup water is added to the system in our leach heap washing cycles.

Leonard:

Other than a small amount of boiler makeup water which is softened by a traditional cation ion exchange system, we do not do anything special to treat our makeup water. We add makeup water to the barren pond and the low preg pond. With our caustic addition we are caustic softening both process liquor and fresh water. After we add caustic the total hardness is about 50 ppm as calcium carbonate.

Daniels:

At Borealis we do not treat our fresh water. Most of our fresh water is used to rinse our heaps. We rinse a heap about once every seven to ten days. The rinse water goes either into the preg or the barren pond to control our inventories. If any scale is formed, it is precipitated in the ponds.

Hartzog:

Paul, at Alligator Ridge you are adding zinc phosphate to the wells. Is zinc carrying through and reporting to the carbon?

Chamberlin:

I'd like Richard Womack, Mill Superintendent at Alligator Ridge to answer that question.

R. Womack - Alligator Ridge:

We have noted that the zinc in the strip liquors has built up from approximately 3 to 5 ppm, to 30 to 40 ppm. It seems to have stabilized at that point.

Hartzog:

Do you continously bleed barren strip solution to the barren pond?

Womack:

No. We use only fresh water makeup and on about a 20 cycle basis we completely replace the strip solution.

Question -

Do you think that pretreatment of fresh water is more important than treatment of process solutions?

Daniels:

Since our experience has indicated that most of the scaling is limited to pump impellers, we have adopted the attitude that treatment of the process solutions adds the product where the problem is most likely to occur.

Leonard:

We realize that we have some pretty bad water, but that is not the source of our scaling problems. If we do not control the alkalinity in the heaps soluble species carbonates go into solution. Our problem is soluble species in the ores, so this is not even really a relevant question. We have to use any scale control on the process liquor.

Gourdie:

At Ortiz, it does not make sense to pretreat the fresh water because we are adding it to the heaps during our wash cycle and in our crushed ore going on to the heaps. We have found that there is essentially no carbonate ion left as the solutions come out of a heap. They contained calcium at about 1,800 ppm. As the pregnant solutions travel down the ditch and into the plant, they pick up carbon dioxide which results in the small amount of scaling we still experience on the carbon.

Chamberlin:

I don't see any big benefits in pretreating water because most of the process streams already carry anti-scaling agents which effectively pretreats the makeup water. This is particularly true at Candelaria, where we have no specialized processes requiring especially clean water. At Alligator Ridge, where we have a strip circuit, there may be a better reason for pretreatment of the water.

Question -

Do you notice any problem when addition of the anti-scaling agent is interrupted? How long can you run without it and is there a radical effect when the addition is interrupted?

Chamberlin:

When we do interrupt these anti-scaling agents for any significant period of time, and by that

I'm talking about days to a week, we notice a substantial build-up in scale. Whether it can be interrupted for four to eight hours at a time with no problem, I am not really sure.

Gourdie:

At Ortiz, we would probably see, within eight hours, a drastic increase in calcium loading on the carbon. We would not have a scaling problem on our pumps and pipelines.

Leonard:

At Northumberland we can see scale buildup in about two days and we can actually measure the effect by taking flowmeter tube checks. We can run a week without mechanical problems.

Daniels:

This happened to us. We had started up our combustion heater and were not adding enough chemical. We were trying to maintain about 3 to 4 ppm. When we started up the barren heater we were watching to see what was going on and we noticed that within three or four days we had scaling problems on our barren pump. This was dramatic to the point where the pump was completely scaled-over, and necessitated breaking down and cleaning the scale from the pump itself. At that time, we increased the dosages and that seemed to have taken care the problem. At that same time we were diluting our solution inventory and had reached a pH of between 9 and 9.5, and that could have contributed to scaling in the pump.

Shoemaker:

Ed Roper, would you please describe your experience with water treatment.

Roper - Zortman-Landusky:

In July 1983 our plugging had gotten to the point where sprinklers were having to be cleaned every 24 hours and we could not keep up. We were acid treating pumps almost every day. We were using phosphonates and they were not working. At the end of July, we changed to polyacrylates and malaic anhydrides. We have two Merrill-Crowe plants five miles apart. The polyacrylates were used at Landusky and the malaic anhydrides were used at Zortman. We had an initial dosage rate of 30 ppm added at the barren pumps of each plant. At that time the calcium content exceeded 90 ppm at both plants. We are now adding only at Landusky and 15 ppm to the barren pumps plus 5 ppm to the preg pump at Zortman. The water sources and the water chemistry are different at Zortman and at Landusky currently our calcium content at both plants is around 30-35 ppm and we anticipate further reductions in the descalant application rates. Both plants use caustic for pH control. During the fall of 1983 we tested lime for pH control to determine what, if any, would be the required increased dosage rate of descalants with the increase in calcium. These tests were indeterminate.

Shoemaker:

Can you comment about the removal of scale after you started the reagents and at what level you started the reagents?

Roper:

In late July 1983, two suppliers were brought in, one to supply polyacrylates, the other to supply malaic anhydrides, and neither of them would guarantee that we would remove scale with the addition of their products. Experience showed that we did remove the scale. We had had a significant build-up of lime in our pipes, for example, our 6" lines were down to 4" and our 8" were down to 6". After the addition of the descalants, the scale in the pipes was removed. We had done nothing to remove the scale other than the addition of the anti-scaling agents.

Shoemaker:

One more question, did you notice the scale coming out all at once or did it dissolve?

Roper:

For the amount of scale that we had in the line we had very little trouble with the dissolving the scale. The effect was very dramatic, in a couple of days our piles went from white to black and we could not see any lime build-up at all.

Shoemaker:

I want to ask Rich Womack about removal of scale.

Womack:

Carlin Gold has a 20 inch decant line under the tailing dam. In the winter of 1978, the line flowed only about 25 gpm. It was plugged with scale. We were desperate because without reclaimed water we could not operate. We began adding hexametaphosphate at a rate of 100 pounds every four hours to the decant tower. In 14 days we removed 50 to 75 tons of calcium carbonate from the decant pipe.

Shoemaker:

Thank you Rich. Ed Roper asked a question about the changing of reagents. Would you take the lead on that, Paul?

Chamberlin:

At Candelaria we started with phosphonate compounds. We had enough plugging of some lines that we had to pig them. When we changed to one of the malaic anhydride compounds, the scaling dissolved. The scale slowly disappeared within a month. We have continued with this reagent and now there is a barely visible scale in pipelines and on pumps. At Alligator Ridge we started out with no anti-scaling agent at all and started using a polyacrylate after about a year.

The deposit also softened and slowly disappeared when the polyacrylate was added. We simply have no problems there now.

Gourdie:

We started with a polyphosphanate and switched to a polyacrylate, primarily because the we had so much trouble feeding the polyphosphanate in cold temperatures. It became very viscous and very hard to work with.

Leonard:

We started out with polyphosphates and found them to be unacceptable to add to the carbon column because there was too much precipitation on the carbon. It was unacceptable to add them to the foot valves of the spray pumps because there wasn't enough retention time and the product caused scale to precipitate continuously through the pump, through the pipeline, and through the sprays. The polyacrylates were tried next. They did a good job in scale removal. We had to remove it from feed to the carbon column because of some carbon fouling. We ran some in-plant tests with polyacrylate and malic anhydride products for seven days. We use a turbine-type mechanical flow meter on the spray line so that was the inspection point examined for scale. We held dosages of 8, 10, 12, 14 and 16 ppm of each product for a week to find out how the scale was doing. They both worked about the same. The malaic anhydride required slightly less dosage to keep the scale from forming and cost us slightly more, so, on a cost basis, they are even. Right now, we are using malaic anhydride and we are adding a total dosage of about 0.022 lbs per ton of solution sprayed. That works out to be about 5 ppm in suction feed to each spray pump, with intermitent addition to the preg solution to the mill.

Daniels:

To listen to everyone else, we do not have a scaling problem per se. We have adopted the attitude that the scale inhibitor that we are adding, which is an organic phosphate, is good insurance during the summertime. It should be stressed here that all three of these chemicals work very well in a side-by-side comparison, they work well together. To have a good test of these chemicals you would have to completely eliminate one type of chemical from the circuit and you would probably endanger your operation by scaling. But they do work together very well.

El Tawil:

Is there any concern about the build-up of organic anti-scalants to the point of causing organic fouling of the carbon, or possible coating of the zinc dust?

Leonard:

We were quite happy with our anti-scale program. The plant was running fine, the carbon columns were doing well and we had no pump problems. The kiln went down and the mill tails started climbing, and in seven days they were, well we were down to 40% recovery and it looked like it was going to get lot worse. We were adding a polyacrylate, at 25 ppm, into the feed to the plant. We got the met lab working and ran a series of adsorption tests. After we shut off the chemical and managed to get our kiln running again we solved the problem by regeneration. Our bottle roll tests showed that indeed we were seeing some drop in the rate of gold absorption with even minimal dosages of polyacrylate. The effect was about a 10% or 12% reduction from what you would expect from virgin carbon. This led us to stop adding polyacrylate. The problem was in the rate of gold loading, it was not in the equilibrium condition loading. With 24 hours of contact time equilibrium loadings were readily achieved. However, we have only 10 minutes to make plant tails as the solution goes through the carbon columns.

Dave Milligan - Anaconda:

What is the pH and the concentration of the water at scaling points?

Chamberlin:

At Candelaria, the pH throughout the circuit is running somewhere betweeen 9.8 and 10.5. At Alligator Ridge, the pH is somewhat higher; in the range of 10.5 to 11.5 throughout the circuit.

Milligan:

Also, the concentrations of the of the calcium and the cabonates and bicarbonates and so forth?

Chamberlin:

At Alligator Ridge, the pregs coming off the heaps contain about 1-2 g/L of calcium. Much of it precipitates in the ditches before it gets to the preg pond, where the concentration is on the order of 200 ppm calcium. We have a 20 to 50 ppm calcium drop after adding makeup cyanide to barren, and what is being pumped back up to the leach heaps as spray solution is running 150 to 200 ppm calcium.

Gourdie:

I do not have too many specific numbers. As I was describing earlier, most of the carbonate precipitates in our heaps but we still have a very high calcium level in the pregnant solution; about 1800 ppm. Our pH throughout the circuit is about 10 to 11.

Leonard:

At Northumberland we are on a caustic soda system. We keep the preg pH above 9.9 or 10 and that means we have to control our spray to a 10.8 minimum pH. If the pH drops to the low 9's which happens as soon as we turn on a new pad or if we get lax in our alkalinity control, we start dissolving bicarbonate out of the rock. We have seen ourselves get into a pH 9.2 situation with heavy rain and at that point there is scale just about everywhere. So, we have got to keep the pH up to keep the solubility of bicarbonate down.

Daniels:

At the Borealis Project we endeavour to keep our pH at about 10.5. In the latest analysis that we did on pregnant solution the calcium was approximately 150 to 200 ppm and the carbonate concentration was between 300 and 400 ppm.

P. Witte - Witteck Development:

Are your operations using white cyanide or black cyanide? Is there any difference in your solution chemistry in using white or black cyanide?

Womack:

At the Carlin Mill, in 1976 we decided to try black cyanide for one year. We noticed no significant difference in the reaction of the cyanide. There was no significant difference in the buildup of the various contaminants. One must remember though, that Carlin Gold solutions have been in closed circuit for roughly 15 years, so the entire periodic table is in solution. The most significant problem that was experienced with the calcium cyanide was in the mixing circuit which was design for sodium cyanide. There was a release of acetylene on mixing and the solution handling was not as clean because of the inert material that was entrained in the calcium cyanide.

T. Downing - Quintana Minerals:

I have experience with Homestake where they used black cyanide and had to stop using it in their sand vat leach systems. Basically, the inert materials present with the black cyanide would actually form a crust on top of the vats. This would seal the vats so they couldn't get any circulation. That is an actual experience and the real problem is from the inert materials that were present with the cyanide.

Shoemaker:

I believe that if you leave a black cyanide drum open for hours there is only about 50% of your cyanide left. It reacts very quickly with moisture and in a black cyanide installation you have to be very careful about dust control and control of the acetylene that is formed.

R. Womack:

The specific question I had for Roger Leonard concerns the comment about carbon poisoning. I run exactly the same reagents you are talking about and we have experienced exactly the opposite results.

I am interested in what you attribute it to? One of the things that I'm becoming more and more aware of is that minor amounts of metallic ion contamination in these circuits is probably as important, if not more important than the amounts of calcium and magnesium.

Leonard:

I will answer the second part first. We know we have copper in solution and as long as we maintain high pH and enough free cyanide in solution we can minimize the copper loading on the carbon. We know we have competition there. If we try to run the plant at a pH of 9 we get copper loading and naturally that reduces gold and silver loading. We have made some tests on organics fouling the carbon and we have good correlation between what happened in the mill and some bottle roll tests with kinetic type data. It is my opinion that the carbon we are working with is so active that if you have a spill any type of organic, it is not going to make it by the first carbon column. The problem that we got into was when the kiln was down we had to bypass the thermal regeneration and in seven days all the carbon that had been up in the lead column was not thermally reactivited. We also have another control point and maybe this is the difference that you see. If the carbonate loadings on the carbon get above 15%; plant tails go up. There are two ways I can control that. I can either acid wash in each cycle, which I do because it is cheaper than the anti-scale chemical, or I can add enough antiscale chemical to keep that carbonate loading down. I can run up to 12% - 14% by weight $CaCO_3$ on the carbon with no detrimental effects. If I go to 16% the tails get bad and if I go to 19% or 20% they are absolutely terrible.

Womack:

It is quite interesting to me because we do have a long chain organic dissolublized due to the pH conditions in the circuit. The barren solution is quite obviously a different color than the preg, so the carbon is loading that organic, but we still do not experience this loss in gold loading.

Leonard:

I wish it did not happen to us.

Hartzog:

I had like to point out one more thing. I was in South Africa two years ago and at one of the properties I visited the kiln was down. As the result of the kiln being down the entire plant was shut down. They had enough oil contamination from underground they were only getting on the order of 10 or 15% absorption on the carbon where they normally get 99.9%. It was strictly the lubricating oil that was coming from underground. Whether it was the oil or the additive that was fouling the carbon no one knew, but they were shut down until the kiln tube was replaced.

Chamberlin:

During the break, Tom DeMull of Alligator Ridge told me that he has run some laboratory tests to determine the effects on the carbon of this anti-scaling agent. It seems to have some small amount of wetting ability. The tests indicate that during the first 20 minutes of loading a fresh batch of carbon the anti-scaling agent's wetting ability actually increase the rate of gold adsorbance on the carbon.

Wayne Shuliger - Calgon Carbon:

I would like to ask Mr. Leonard. When you came back on stream, to reactivate the carbon, did you change any conditions in the kiln?

Leonard:

No. Not at that time.

Schulliger:

I guess it is an indirect fired kiln that you have.

Leonard:

Correct.

Schuliger:

Do you add any air at all in your kiln or do you have a loose fitting that could be sucking air in with your carbon?

Leonard:

We try to minimize the air intake by submerging the kiln discharge under water. Then the only air leak we have in the kiln is a poor fitting door. In other words, we cut it way down.

Schuliger:

And nothing at the feed end?

Leonard:

Nothing other than a free floating metal ring seal.

Question -

"Variations in Water Treatment in Response to Weather."

Daniels:

During the summer months, the Borealis Project has one addition point, the preg solution sump, and by adding the chemical there that takes care of our clarifiers and filter presses. The flow through the plant is approximately 300 gallons/minute and we treat with 10 ml/minute of product. This maintains an approximate total phosphate concentration of 2.5 to 3.5 ppm. During the winter months, when our barren heater is running, we have to increase our addition points. In addition to the preg sump we have another at the barren solution sump at the same 10 ml/minute

rate and another 10 ml/minute at the booster sump before the pads to keep our sprinkler lines free. So, overall, in the winter time we're adding about 30 ml/minute to maintain a 3 to 4 ppm phosphate concentration.

Hartzog:

You are changing your water treatment in response to combustion products rather than chemical changes due to temperature. Is that right?

Daniels:

Yes. After the barren heater our pH will drop from 10.5 to as low as 7.5 and our cyanide consumption is very high. During the winter months, when the barren heater is going, we have to add both makeup cyanide and caustic to maintain solution strength. There is a night and day difference with the barren heater.

Leonard:

Since we have our anti-scale program straightened out, we're running the same dosage now as we did in February, but I do not think we have enough historical data to answer that question.

Gourdie:

Ortiz feeds the same amount summer and winter, at the same locations.

Chamberlin:

Candelaria and Alligator Ridge feed about the same amount of anti-scalant in both summer and winter.

Question:

In your experience are there any differences in scaling rates or types of scale when using lime or caustic for pH control and does the addition of cement change the response of the other two?

Chamberlin:

Candelaria has used a sodium system since its beginning, and the main scale component has been calcium carbonate. In spite of the fact that the ore is siliceous, and much of the silver is encapsulated in silica, we have not noticed any silica problems using the sodium system.

At Alligator Ridge, we started with sodium hydroxide and then changed to lime after about a year and a half. With the change to lime came an increase in the rate of scale build up. The increase in the quantity of the scale is complicated by the fact that we encountered more acidic ores in the Vantage 2 pit and had to change to lime because caustic costs where just too high. We have more scale, but we are not certain if it is the result of changing to lime or is due to the nature of the ore. It is probably a combination of both. Precipitation of calcium carbonate on the carbon built up very slowly when we first started operations. This was when we were using the sodium hydroxide. In fact, we eventually had so much scale on the carbon that we had to remove the carbon from the circuit and replace it with a fresh load. This happened before we put in the acid wash circuit. Now even with the addition of lime at Alligator Ridge, we do not have a serious problem simply because the acid wash circuit and the addition of the anti-scaling agent seem to be keeping it under control.

Gourdie:

Ortiz has always used lime for pH control. Last winter when we were heating our barren solution directly and experiencing a pH drop, we were recovering that pH with caustic. Our solutions were so saturated with carbonate ions that we were even precipitating sodium carbonate and we could see bands and layers of calcium carbonate and sodium carbonate.

Leonard:

Way back in 1981 and 1982 Northumberland made the switch from lime to caustic for alkalinity control and that really did not solve any of the scale problems. We have been able to handle the scale caused with the caustic circuit and now we are starting to agglomerate the ore with cement. We expect problems to change around a little bit. From the lab data and the initial solution returns we know that water hardness is going to rise but we hope to control the scale.

Daniels:

To make up our mill solution at startup we used caustic for pH control and after that our cement in agglomeration circuit maintains our pH except in the winter time. At one time we were adding lime directly to the barren sump, which could have contributed to the fouling of the barren sump pump almost immediately. After we cleaned out the barren pump a couple of times we decided it would be best to add lime at the number one collection point before the preg pond. So, I do not believe we have any real comparison between caustic soda and cement and/or lime.

Tom Enos - Carlin Gold -

We did notice a significant increase in scaling when we made the addition of cement. We were getting 30% fouling on our carbon. We have always been on lime at Carlin. The only area that we tried caustic was at Bootstrap and we did it for a scaling problem there. The scaling problem, to some degree, went away. We were using a phosphate at the time for scale control and the problem we had with going to caustic was we could not make a barren in our carbon columns. We were eluting the gold back off the carbon with the caustic.

At Maggie Creek we added lime to the barren solution. When we encountered the percolation problems we started agglomerating with cement and we reduced lime to the point where it was insignificant. When we did that there was a significant difference in scaling. It was calcium silicate scale that was the problem. It was coming from the cement. So we went to acid wash and changed the whole circuit because of the cement.

Question -

Has precipitation of salts or carbonates affected the percolation rates in your heaps, and, if so, describe the problems.

Daniels:

It is observed that towards the end of a leaching cycle there is a deposition of carbonates or salts and they appear as a white coating on the heap. At this time we are usually ready to take the pad off leach. So if this has an effect on the percolation rate, it has not been observed.

Leonard:

We too see the white carbonate scale on top of the heaps and we rip the surface before we releach. We noticed that there was quite a bit of cementing of top particles and it was hard for a D-9 with a nine foot shank to make one complete pass. Actually we had to back off to about a seven foot rip depth. This pad percolated fine. We could get solution through at a rate of 0.004 gallons per minute per square foot. Most of the differences in percolation we see are just different ore types.

Gourdie:

We have similar experience at Ortiz. There was one occasion when we had some blinding due to some kind of precipitate. We had it analyzed and it appeared to be some kind of copper cyanide compound. After ripping we see no difference and essentially we do not feel we have any problems with precipitates. Ortiz, I might add, has very little fines in their ore; less than 3% minus 100 mesh material.

Chamberlin:

At Candelaria we had a calcium carbonate scaling problem in the early days. It was necessary to keep the heap surfaces wet so that the solutions could percolate through the scale and to rip them very well before building another lift on top. Since using the anti-scaling agents, however, we have not noticed much calcium carbonate on top of the heap, and we have not had any percolation problems. We do routinely rip with a 10 foot single shank on a D-9 and have not noticed that ripping gives us much additional silver recovery. We do it as a precautionary measure.

At Alligator Ridge, the precipitation of calcium carbonate is obvious as a relatively porous white coating on the heaps but it does not appear to slow down the percolation rates. We had some scaling problems on the sprinklers, especially the Rainbird type. We replaced them with wobblers and do not have any problems with them now. We also rip the ore using a 10 foot deep shank. Our experience has been that ripping seems to give an extra couple per cent of extraction if we continue leaching on that ripped heap.

Question –

Have you any experience with wetting agents as an aid in speeding up leach rates, percolation rates, or extraction?

Chamberlin:

Alligator Ridge has done some testwork along these lines, but the results are quite inconclusive.

Gourdie:

Ortiz has run some column tests using wetting agents and found no benefit from them. However, this was when we were in oxide ore. We have extremely good percolation in our ore anyway. We are getting into some deeper sulphide material where the rock is much more competent and we are interested in running some more tests to see if a wetting agent will improve recovery.

Leonard:

We have some poorly percolating heaps and think that probably the real solution is to build them right from the onset. We started to look into this for remedial action. We have not gotten very far yet. We set up our test program in two phases. One would be scoping tests to find if any of these organic things foul carbon. The second phase would be to run some column tests and see if there is any noticeable difference in the percolation rate of the same ore type. We have not gotten by phase one yet. We have not found anything that does not have an effect on the carbon.

Daniels:

To date, Borealis has not used any wetting agents. We get 75% of our recoverable gold within the first week of leaching. This issue has not been a major concern to us.

Question –

To what quality should water be demineralized before using for carbon strip solution?

Daniels:

With the zinc precipitation system we do not address that problem at all.

Leonard:

We do not demineralize our makeup water to the stripping circuit. The bleed stream runs anywhere from 7 to 15% and we try to maintain as much of that water as we can with holding tanks. The water is naturally softened by the caustic addition. We run the reagents at 0.1% cyanide and 1% caustic. We do notice some slime precipitate from the reagents in the bottom of the preg and the lean tanks. As of this date we have not had to pump them out.

Gourdie:

Ortiz does not treat the water for stripping. We do displace about 2,000 gallons from each strip cycle into our first absorption tank. We have not noticed any buildup of precipitate in our tank.

Chamberlin:

I am not sure what the quality of the water should be. It seems that as we add clean water to the stripping circuit it is going to be contaminated almost immediately by contaminants that are on the carbon.

Question –

Is Acid Washing Necessary for Carbon After Every Stripping Cycle?" "Which Acid Should One Use?", "Should One Acid Wash Before or After Thermal Reactivation?
Chamberlin:

Alligator Ridge does not acid wash after every cycle. We acid wash only when the barren solution climbs to a level of 0.008-0.009 oz per ton. We normally operate in the 0.004 range. Over the past year or so we have probably washed on the order of one batch out of twenty. The carbon is loaded to about 150 ozs. per ton. We wash with nitric acid before sending the carbon to the kiln.

Gourdie:

Ortiz acid washs after each strip cycle following the kiln with nitric acid. There's a lot of debate as to whether one should use nitric or hydrochloric before the kiln or before the strip. On a recent visit to South Africa I was most impressed with their stripping process there. They acid wash in their strip vessel, usually with hydrochloric before stripping and they get very rapid stripping.

Leonard:

We take about a third of the carbon from the strip lot, put it through the kiln, then all of the carbon goes to washing with hydrochloric before it goes back into the last carbon column. The reason why we go to the kiln with only about a third of the carbon is to maintain good reactivation. The throughput of the kiln is limited to about 50 to 60 lbs per hour. We had been using nitric acid to wash carbon and we found that hydrochloric acid leaves the carbon in better shape and partially reactivates the carbon.

Leonard Harris - Newmont Mining Corporation:

I did not hear very much said about the heating of solutions, directly or indirectly. Would the panel like to comment?

Chamberlin:

We tried heating solution at Alligator Ridge and we do not do it any more because of the cost. It simply was not a cost effective approach to maintaining operations during cooler weather. The primary costs are caustic, because of losing alkalinity to a more acidic solution, and sodium cyanide, because a very high percentage of it is destroyed in the heating operation. I am referring to a submerged combustion system, not a low temperature heat exchanger system.

Gourdie:

Ortiz began heating the solutions for the first time last winter. We used to lose as much as 6 weeks a year of spray time. We were successful in eliminating that problem. However, we did experience high cyanide and caustic consumption. However, by using the heat exchanger method we are going to this winter we will not have the cost of the cyanide and caustic. We think it is going to be very cost-effective for Ortiz.

Otto Walls - Smoky Valley:

Well, we went to indirect fire last year. It is very hard to compare one winter to another. We lost spray time that would have amounted to 8 days total the whole winter season. Comparing previous January's doré production, the highest was January 1978, at about 5,000 ozs. with January 1983 when we produced over 11,000 ozs of doré; indirect solution heating was a significant help to us. Direct firing did scale up all the lines so that by January, in a normal winter season, the flow rates would decrease to the point that low flow apparently hurt the operation. We had to break a half mile of Drisco pipe in the summer time to remove calcium carbonate. I think part of the success is the ability to maintain full flow rate to the pads with indirect heating. You have to learn to play the weather and if it looks like it is really going to get cold at night start the heating unit.

Leonard:

Otto Walls stated that Smoky Valley only lost 8 days to weather in 1983 using their submerged heater. Under exactly the same weather conditions (being 25 miles apart) we could only maintain a 59% spray availability in January and February even with flood leaching because of freezing pipes.

Shoemaker:

I want to ask Otto the size of their submerged

exhaust burners. I believe that they have two 12,500,000 btu/hr burners installed.

Walls:

Yes.

Gourdie:

We have one 10,000,000 btu/hr burner

Shoemaker:

How much fuel are you using?

Walls:

About 200 gallons per hour of No. 2 Diesel. The way it works out is a cost of about 10 ounces of gold per day cost to produce 200 or more ounces.

Fred de Vries - Dupont:

We destroy cyanide in our plant at about 150° Celcius. So, I think it's important, in trying to heat these solutions, to be sure that you do not get very high temperature peaks. So, as a design feature I think you ought to avoid excessive high temperatures.

Bernie Stennus - Consultant:

At what temperatures do you feel that you have to turn on your heating equipment, and what to temperatures do you heat your solutions.

Chamberlin:

I want to add that what we were talking about earlier was direct submerged combustion, as opposed to the lower temperature heat exchanger approach taken by Smoky Valley.

Womack:

At Alligator it depends directly on sprinkler type when you get down to freezing temperatures. Rainbirds are good to 28°F, they are operable to 23°F, but you lose about 50% of your rotating elements. With wobblers we have gone as low 13 degrees above zero and have experienced no loss in sprinklers but the heaps finally iced to the point where it was ridiculous to continue spraying because we had an ice cap.

When we heated, we designed for 40 degrees rise. As far as I am concerned, as long as you are in the 38 to 40 degree temperature range you are better off than if you are higher in temperature because of deoxygenation of the solution which will then cause it to freeze quicker when you get into the freezing situations.

Hartzog:

Your major concern early on is the sprinklers plugging up, not blinding with ice.

Womack:

Yes. Again that depends on sprinkler design.
When you go to the wobbler which has one operating
part and a direct open orifice, you do not have
this kind of a problem.

Gourdie:

Also the wobbler makes a larger droplet, so
you'd have less cooling effect as it's being
sprayed.

At Ortiz we will start heating solutions if we
think the temperatures are going to get down to
around to 26 to 28 degrees at night. We found
that if could get the solution to the point
furthest away from where we were inducing the heat
to 40 degress Fahrenheit we would not have a
serious freezing problem. Eventually we would
build up quite a heat sink inside this 200,000
tons of ore on the leach pads. Hence, we used
that as a guideline as to how high we have to heat
the solutions that we're sending out.

Shoemaker:

I'd like to ask, what is the efficiency of the
heat exchangers? I believe you all use the same
heat exchanger.

Walls:

I'd like to address the previous question a
little bit. I disagree with Rich. The most
important factor as to freezing or not is the wind
velocity down the valley. That is why you have to
keep watching the weather predictions and decide
which way to go at any particular time. We will
definitely have the heater on at anything below 30
degrees Fahrenheit. You can start forming ice
below 28 degrees Fahrenheit, regardless of the
temperature you are heating your solution to if
you have a 60 MPH wind running down the valley.
Smoky Valley, if you're not aware, is about a 5
mile wide valley between two mountain ranges that
rise about 6,000 feet above the base elevation.
Last winter we had one or two days where it
dropped down to 5 degrees above zero and we were
able to keep heating and leave the sprinklers on
as long as there was a dead wind condition.

We have seen no appreciable difference in the
final solution temperature coming out of the
system, so we estimate our efficiency at 96-98 per
cent. We see about a 20 degree temperature rise.
We normally run the solution to the heater at
about 40 degrees Fahrenheit and feed solutions to
the pads up to about 60 degrees Fahrenheit. That
is at approximately 2000 gpm.

Hartzog:

I understand you use caustic in the solution
that you are heating directly

Walls:

Back when we direct fired, I could not figure

out why one of the water contaminants was sulphate
ion. Once we started running the heater with the
heat exchanger we realized the sulphur content in
the fuel was making sulphuric acid. That is what
rapidly corroded some metal parts in the
recirculating system to the heat exchanger. By
adding caustic we keep the pH up to about 9 and
minimize corrosion.

Shoemaker:

And what level of caustic consumption do you
have?

Walls:

We just put it in by hand last year and
maintained the pH. We also had a small bleed
system to keep anything from building up in
there. This year we have gone to an automatic
control off the liquid caustic system for the
plant, so we might get a little bit better handle
on what we have to do to maintain pH.

Harris:

Do you make a bleed of the solution that you
are heating? I understand that to overcome the
problem originally you went from lime to caustic
in the main solution. Are you going back to lime
now, and, if you have, do you get any scaling on
the outside of the heat exchanger?

Walls:

Yes, we do run a small bleed on the system
recirculating to the heat exchanger. Basically we
just did that because when we first started,
before we started adding reagents, the water got
very red with iron salts and we wanted to clear it
up. We just continued it as a good process.

We had converted to sodium hydroxide and we are
just presently looking at converting back to
lime. We are taking the approach that Ortiz has
in trying to mix dry lime onto the ore, evenly
distributing it into the ore pile and hope that
any scale formation will be in the ore. The real
reason for this approach is not because we are
dissatisfied with sodium hydroxide for alkalinity
control, but because we have moved into other
zones in the pit and have seen great increases in
clay content. We feel that the sodium hydroxide
was causing the clay to swell and not helping with
permeability.

Larry Cenegy - N.L. Treating Chemicals:

I would just like to comment that the type of
chemical that is being used, for instance at the
Borealis Project, is not a polyphosphate. It is
as described earlier, an organic phosphate.
Polyphosphates are, to some extent, older
technology chemicals, which are still in use, but
have very limited application. If any of the
speakers who described experiences with
polyphosphates and phosphonates would care to
comment on this, I would appreciate it.

Bill Faulkner - Calgon Carbon:

I would like to make a couple of comments. One is about nitric acid as it relates to use just use around activated carbon. It has not happened to my knowledge in the gold industry, but there can be a reaction between concentrated nitric acid and activated carbon, strong enough to create an explosive force. So, I just mention that as a caution.

Hartzog:

What is concentrated?

Faulkner:

Where there have been explosions, the acid was very concentrated. I don't know of any problems at less than, say, 15%. I also have a hunch that nitric acid, to some degree, weakens the structure of the carbon. You've got an oxidant and carbon together, and they want to react. There is another safety consideration around activated carbon. Personnel entering tanks or columns containing wet carbon are at risk. Wet carbon in confined spaces depletes the atmosphere of oxygen, and that has resulted in some fatalities in years gone by. In reference to South African practice, I think that one deserves some mention. I was there recently. They use HCl ahead of stripping, so that chloride ion in the kiln is not a problem.

Unknown Speaker:

I'd like to know if anyone has had experience with washing the carbon with acid, say, halfway through the absorption cycle?

Leonard:

We had a problem about two months ago when a rain storm dropped about three quarters of an inch of rain in twenty hours. We picked up about 8,000-10,000 tons of water in our pond system which threw our alkalinity all out of whack. We were generating about 700 lbs day of scale on the carbon and the plant tail started to go sky high. One of the ways to solve this was to put some anti-scale chemical back into the feed to the carbon columns and the other was to hurry and try to get more caustic onto the leach pads. For an immediate cure, we re-routed our eduction system and sent carbon from the middle of the circuit to acid washing and then back out. We had some interesting profiles of gold and silver absorption by just taking off the scale. We did help our silver recovery by acid washing in the middle of the circuit. It appears that the carbon, after it was acid washed, acted like barren carbon that we added back into the circuit. There was a marked reduction in both gold and silver solutions grades going through the circuit.

Hartzog:

Ray Davidson of Anglo in South Africa is a great proponent of interstage acid washing of CIP carbon, which would apply to heap leach carbon. Unfortunately, Ray is not here.

With that, we'll close. On behalf of Bob and myself, I want to express our personal thanks and appreciation to the panelists, their sponsoring companies and to the vendors of water treatment chemicals who have contributed to the session. The session is closed.

LANDUSKY SPRAY SOLUTION
15 ppm of Polyacrylates

CONSTITUENT	mg/1
Potassium	11
Sodium	1,060
Calcium	29
Magnesium	7
Sulfate	987
Chloride	322
Carbonate	308
Bicarbonate	940
Total Dissolved Solids @ 180°C	3,220
Total Solids, Calculated	3,190
Total Hardness as CaCO3	100
Alkalinity as CaCO3	1,280
Ammonia as N	29.1
Nitrate + Nitrite as N	79.0
Cyanide	327
Fluoride	4.1
Silica as SiO2	15.5
Chemical Oxygen Demand	279
Total Organic Carbon	40
Turbidity, NTU	33
Total Suspended Solids	131
Conductivity @ 25°C, umhos/cm	4,330
pH	9.3

METALS (TOTAL):	mg/1
Aluminum	0.5
Arsenic	0.620
Barium	< 0.1
Beryllium	< 0.005
Baron	< 0.1
Cadmium	0.016
Chromium	< 0.02
Cobalt	2.16
Copper	108
Iron	2.66
Gold	0.15
Lead	0.01
Manganese	0.12
Mercury	0.021
Molybdenum	0.532
Nickel	2.38
Selenium	0.112
Silver	0.327
Strontium	0.2
Tin	0.26
Titanium	< 0.01
Vanadium	< 0.10
Zinc	102

ZORTMAN PLANT SOLUTION FEED PUMP
5 ppm of Malaic Anhydride

CONSTITUENT	mg/1
Potassium	14
Sodium	1,100
Calcium	37
Magnesium	11
Sulfate	850
Chloride	268
Carbonate	375
Bicarbonate	695
Total Dissolved Solids @ 180°C	3,450
Total Solids, Calculated	3,000
Total Hardness as CaCO3	136
Alkalinity as CaCO3	1,190
Ammonia as N	30.7
Nitrate + Nitrite as N	158
Cyanide	288
Fluoride	7.2
Silica as SiO2	18.0
Chemical Oxygen Demand	268
Total Organic Carbon	52
Turbidity, NTU	1.4
Total Suspended Solids	7
Conductivity @ 25°C, umhos/cm	4,520
pH	9.3

METALS (TOTAL):	mg/1
Aluminum	< 0.1
Arsenic	0.180
Barium	< 0.1
Beryllium	< 0.005
Baron	< 0.1
Cadmium	0.034
Chromium	< 0.02
Cobalt	2.62
Copper	35.2
Iron	0.53
Gold	0.49
Lead	< 0.02
Manganese	0.11
Mercury	0.072
Molybdenum	0.361
Nickel	2.04
Selenium	0.030
Silver	0.732
Strontium	0.2
Tin	0.3
Titanium	< 0.01
Vanadium	< 0.10
Zinc	88.3

ZORTMAN SPRAY SOLUTION
5 ppm of Malaic Anhydride

CONSTITUENT	mg/1
Potassium	12
Sodium	1,240
Calcium	33
Magnesium	8
Sulfate	849
Chloride	415
Carbonate	528
Bicarbonate	638
Total Dissolved Solids @ 180°C	3,600
Total Solids, Calculated	3,400
Total Hardness as $CaCO_3$	116
Alkalinity as $CaCO_3$	1,400
Ammonia as N	31.1
Nitrate + Nitrite as N	162
Cyanide	378
Fluoride	7.6
Silica as SiO_2	23.7
Chemical Oxygen Demand	333
Total Organic Carbon	52
Turbidity, NTU	12
Total Suspended Solids	47
Conductivity @ 25°C, umhos/cm	4,700
pH	9.4

METALS (TOTAL):	mg/1
Aluminum	0.5
Arsenic	0.280
Barium	< 0.1
Beryllium	< 0.005
Baron	< 0.1
Cadmium	0.017
Chromium	< 0.02
Cobalt	2.47
Copper	34.9
Iron	1.10
Gold	0.14
Lead	0.18
Manganese	0.37
Mercury	0.030
Molybdenum	0.392
Nickel	2.14
Selenium	0.037
Silver	0.348
Strontium	0.22
Tin	0.2
Titanium	< 0.01
Vanadium	< 0.10
Zinc	104

INDEX

V

Vacuum, 112, 114
Van der Waals forces, 133
van Zyl, D., 59

W

War Production Board Order L-208, 25
Water
  brackish, purifying by diffusion, 142
  chemistry of heap leaching operations
    (panel discussion), 139
  demineralizing, 142, 152
  fresh, pretreatment of, 145
  pH, concentration of at scaling points, 148
  sea
    desalting, 142

purifying by diffusion, 142
softening processes, 142
treatment, 142, 144
  magnetic, 145
  variations in with response to weather,
    150
Water Quality Control Board (WQCB),
    California, 32, 35, 38, 61
Wetting agents, 152
Windfall plant, Nevada, 6
Womack, R.A., 9

Y

Yelomine
  coupling, 26

distribution lines, 26
Yelomine PVC pipe, 44

Z

Zadra technique, 101
Zinc
  cementation, 96
  consumption, 4, 27, 35, 98
  feed rates, 112, 114
  precipitation, 4, 5, 31, 95, 111
    capital costs of, 27
    dust, 38
    parameters, optimization of, 109
Zortman-Landusky Mining Co., Montana, 3,
    5, 7, 25